621.317

**Power
Technology
Centre**

NEWNES

CENTRAL ELECTRICITY GENERATING BC
Research and Development Departme

D0610440

885419000.

NEWNES ELECTRICAL POCKET BOOK

NEWNES
ELECTRICAL
POCKET BOOK

Edited by
E. A. REEVES
D.F.H.(Hons.), C.Eng., M.I.E.E.

CENTRAL ELECTRICITY
STUDENTS
LIBRARY
S 515844
GENERATING BOARD

CENTRAL ELECTRICITY
STUDENTS
LIBRARY
S4 22531
GENERATING BOARD

LONDON
GEORGE NEWNES LIMITED
TOWER HOUSE, SOUTHAMPTON ST., W.C.2

© George Newnes Ltd.

1937, 1938, 1939, 1942, 1943, 1944, 1945,
1946, 1947, 1948, 1950, 1952, 1953, 1955,
1957, 1960, 1967

Sixteenth Edition 1967

C. E. G. B.
M. E. L. LIBRARY
MARCHWOOD.

Printed in Great Britain by Butler & Tanner Ltd., Frome and London

PREFACE

In the previous edition of this Pocket Book many new advances were mentioned which have since then been developed and have become a part of electrical engineering technology. For instance, commercial nuclear power which, in 1960, was still very much in its infancy is now entering its second stage of development in that the advanced gas-cooled reactor is to be used in the second generation of nuclear stations being built for the C.E.G.B. It will be recalled that the first stage was based upon the use of the Magnox reactor, a gas-cooled graphite-moderated system.

Pumped storage schemes and desalination of sea water are associated with nuclear power and both are very much in the forefront today. The 400 MW Cruachan pumped storage scheme was inaugurated in October 1965, when the first 100 MW vertical-shaft pumping/generating unit was commissioned.

Desalination is a process whereby sea water is converted into fresh water suitable for drinking purposes. There is an increasing need for more pure water to meet the requirements of the rapidly expanding population of the earth. Britain has a unique part to play in providing such water because she is a leader in both the field of desalination and generation of power by nuclear means. This latter function is necessary because of the large amounts of heat needed in the flash distillation method of desalination as pioneered and used by the British.

The size of turbo-generators used in this country has increased considerably over the past five years. Power stations now being built are incorporating sets of 500 MW capacity, the first such unit having been commissioned in Ferrybridge C Power Station in February 1966. Even larger super-critical sets of 660 MW rating are being built while designs of 750 MW and 1,000 MW are on the drawing board. The modern British power station of the 1970's will have an installed capacity of 2,000 MW and in some cases up to 4,000 MW. Generation voltages of these larger sets will also rise to something over 20 kV.

Solar power has progressed beyond the research stage and it is quite usual for it to be used as a source of power in space research vehicles. Industrial applications, however, are still in the embryo stage. Magnetohydrodynamics, a means of generating electricity direct, is attracting more attention with a 200 MW (thermal) unit planned.

Plastics is finding an increasing use in the electrical industry so the opportunity has been taken of extending this section of the book by including references to such material as p.t.f.e.

Much has been written and said about earth-loop and neutral-loop impedance testing and it is by no means clear as to the best method to adopt ; this is in spite of the I.E.E. Regulations on the subject. Thus, whilst certain procedures have been suggested, it is not claimed that these are the only methods available. Indeed specialists who took part in the I.E.E. Colloquium on the subject held in March 1965 disagreed in some measure with each other. Nevertheless the Pocket Book suggestions will, it is believed, command general support among electrical engineers.

Standardization of motor dimensions is a very important subject to all engineers and much work has been done in this field during the last five years. New British Standards have been issued and consequently more information has become available.

Considerable advances have been recorded in the application of semi-conductor devices to the electric motor. From the small-power transistor has developed the high-power thyristor capable of supplying bulk d.c. power for large variable-speed motor-drive systems. In addition to this, it is now possible to convert from one frequency to another so there exists the possibility of variable-speed a.c. motor being supplied from these devices. Other possible applications for this semiconductor device are mentioned in the appropriate section in the book.

Increasing productivity is urged by all in authority these days and to some extent this increase is dependent upon good lighting. Therefore, the table on recommended values of illumination has been greatly extended to cover as many industries as possible. The Glare Index factor has been incorporated in this table for the first time.

The advantages of superconductivity have always been realized but the difficulty of exploiting the phenomena has prevented it being applied to the heavy electrical industry. However, recent developments have enabled at least one manufacturer to design a transformer operating in the region of superconductivity.

All other chapters have been checked and brought up-to-date where necessary, and many new illustrations and tables have been included.   E. A. REEVES

CONTENTS

CONTENTS (*continued*)

NEWNES ELECTRICAL
POCKET BOOK

THE chief function of any engineer's pocket book is the presentation in convenient form of facts, tables and formulae relating to the particular branch of engineering dealt with.

In the case of electrical engineering, it is essential that the engineer should have a clear understanding of the methods by which the various formulae are derived in order that he can be quite certain that any particular formula is applicable to the conditions which he is considering. This applies with particular force in the case of alternating current work.

The preliminary sections of the Pocket Book have, therefore, been devoted to the theoretical groundwork upon which all the practical applications are based.

Again, when an engineer is called upon to deal with any particular type of electrical apparatus, for example, a protective relay system, a thermostatically controlled heating system, or industrial switchgear and control gear, the first requirement is that he shall understand the principles upon which these systems operate. In order to provide this information, much space has been devoted in the various sections to clear descriptions of the circuits and principles which are used in the different types of electrical apparatus.

The inclusion of technical descriptions, together with the essential data embodied in the tables, will be found to provide the ideal combination for those engineers engaged on the utilization side of the industry, where many different types of equipment and electrical appliances, ranging from mercury-arc rectifiers to electrode steam boilers, may have to be specified, installed and maintained in efficient operation.

Throughout the Pocket Book due regard has been paid to the requirements of the Institution of Electrical Engineers' Regulations for the Electrical Equipment of Buildings, 14th Edition, 1966.

GRAPHICAL SYMBOLS

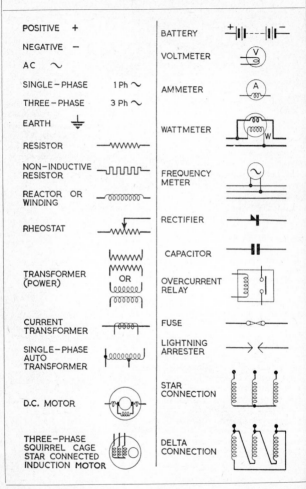

POSITIVE   +

NEGATIVE   −

AC $\sim$

SINGLE – PHASE   1 Ph $\sim$

THREE – PHASE   3 Ph $\sim$

EARTH   ⏚

RESISTOR

NON – INDUCTIVE
RESISTOR

REACTOR OR
WINDING

RHEOSTAT

TRANSFORMER
(POWER)   OR

CURRENT
TRANSFORMER

SINGLE – PHASE
AUTO
TRANSFORMER

D.C. MOTOR

THREE – PHASE
SQUIRREL CAGE
STAR CONNECTED
INDUCTION MOTOR

BATTERY

VOLTMETER

AMMETER

WATTMETER

FREQUENCY
METER

RECTIFIER

CAPACITOR

OVERCURRENT
RELAY

FUSE

LIGHTNING
ARRESTER

STAR
CONNECTION

DELTA
CONNECTION

FUNDAMENTALS

Current.—The term "current" is used to denote the rate at which electricity flows. In the case of a steady flow the current is given by the quantity of electricity which passes a given point in one second. The magnitude of the current depends not only upon the electromotive force but also upon the nature and dimensions of the path through which it circulates.

Ohm's Law.—Ohm's law states that the current in a d.c. circuit varies in direct proportion to the voltage and is inversely proportional to the resistance of the circuit. By choosing suitable units this law may be written

$$\text{Current} = \frac{\text{electromotive force}}{\text{resistance}}.$$

The commercial units for these quantities are

Current—the ampere	(A)
Electromotive force—the volt	(V)
Resistance—the ohm	(Ω)

Using the symbols I, V and R to represent the above quantities in the order given, Ohm's law can be written

$$I = \frac{V}{R}$$

or $\qquad\qquad V = I \times R.$

The law not only holds for a complete circuit, but can be applied for any part of a circuit providing care is taken to use the correct values for that part of the circuit.

Specific Resistance.—The specific resistance of any material is the resistance of a piece of material having unit length and unit sectional area. This value is also termed the resistivity. The symbol is ρ. Both centimetre and inch units are used and these can be converted by the following formula :

$$\rho \text{ in inch units} = \frac{1}{2\cdot54}\rho \text{ in centimetre units.}$$

The specific resistance of a material is not usually constant but depends on the temperature. The table is given on page 5 showing the specific resistance of the more usual metals and alloys.

Resistance of a Conductor.—The resistance of a uniform conductor, with sectional area A, and length l is given by

$$R = \rho\frac{l}{A}.$$

The units used must be inches and square inches if ρ is in inch units and centimetres and square centimetres if ρ is in centimetre units.

Temperature Coefficient.—The resistance of a conductor at any temperature can be found as follows :

$$R_t = R_o(1 + \alpha t).$$

$R_t =$ resistance at temperature $t°$ C
$R_o =$,,   ,,   ,, $o°$ C

The coefficient α is called the temperature coefficient and it can be described as the ratio of the increase in resistance per degree C rise in temperature compared with the actual resistance at $o°$ C.

The coefficient for copper may be taken as 0·004. The increase in resistance for rise of temperature is important, and for many calculations this point *must* be taken into account.

Power.—Power is defined as the rate of doing work. The electrical unit of power (P) is the *watt* (abbreviation W). and taking a steady current as with d.c.,

        1 watt = 1 volt × 1 ampere
or   watts = volts × amperes
or in symbols $P = V \times I.$

(For alternating current, see section on a.c.)
Note.—1 kilowatt = 1,000 watts.

Energy.—Energy can be defined as power × time, and electrical energy is obtained from

$$\text{Energy} = VIt$$

where t is the time in seconds.

The unit obtained will be in joules, which is equivalent to 1 ampere at 1 volt for 1 second. The practical unit for energy is the kilowatt-hour (Board of Trade Unit) and is given by $\dfrac{\text{watts} \times \text{hours}}{1000} = \text{kWh.}$

4

the square of the distance between them). This may be written

$$F = \frac{q_1 q_2}{4\pi\epsilon_0 d^2} \text{ newtons}$$

where q_1 and q_2 are the charges in coulombs and d the distance in metres—the space in between the charges being either air or a vacuum with a permittivity ϵ_0.

If the two charged bodies are separated by some other medium the force acting may be different, depending on the relative permittivity of the *dielectric* between the two charged bodies. The relative permittivity is also termed the dielectric constant.

In this case the force is given by

$$F = \frac{q_1 q_2}{4\pi\epsilon_r \epsilon_0 d^2}$$

where ϵ_r is the constant for the particular dielectric. For air or a vacuum the value of ϵ_r is unity.

Intensity of Field.—There is an electrostatic field due to any charged body and the *intensity* of this field is taken as the force on unit charge.

The intensity of field at any given point due to an electrostatic charge is given by

$$E = \frac{q}{4\pi\epsilon_0 d^2} \text{ volts per metre.}$$

Note : In the m.k.s. system the ampere is the defined unit, and not the unit of charge as is the case of the c.g.s. system. Hence a coulomb is defined as that quantity of electricity which flows past a given point of a circuit when a current of one ampere is maintained for one second.

The value of the ampere, adopted internationally in 1948, is defined as that current which, when flowing in each of two infinitely long parallel conductors in a vacuum, separated by one metre between centres, causes each conductor to have a force acting upon it of 2×10^{-7} newton per metre length of conductor. The definition on the basis of the silver voltameter is now obsolete.

Dielectric Flux. The field due to a charge as referred to above is assumed to be due to imaginary *tubes of force* similar to magnetic lines of force, and these tubes are the paths which would be taken by a free unit charge if acted on by the charge of the body concerned.

By means of these tubes of force we get a *dieletric flux-density* of so many tubes of force per square metre of area.

For our unit we take a sphere 1 metre radius and give it unit charge of electricity. We then get a dielectric flux density on the surface of the sphere of unity = one tube of force per square centimetre. The total number of tubes of force will be equal to the surface area of the sphere = 4π. For any charge q at a distance r the dielectric flux density will be

$$D = \frac{q}{4\pi r^2} \text{ coulombs per sq. metre.}$$

We have seen that the intensity of field or electric force at any point is

$$E = \frac{q}{4\pi\epsilon_0\epsilon_r r^2}$$

so that this can also be stated as $E = D/\epsilon_r\epsilon_0$

Electrostatic Potential.—The potential to which a body is raised by an electric charge is proportional to the charge and the *capacity* of the body—so that $C = Q/V$, where V is the potential and C the capacity. The definition of the capacity of a body is taken as the charge or quantity of electricity necessary to raise the potential by one m.k.s. unit. This unit of potential is the work done in joules, in bringing unit charge (1 coulomb) from infinity to a point at unit potential.

Capacitance.—The actual measurement of capacity is termed *capacitance*, and for practical purposes the unit is arranged for use with volts and coulombs. In this case the unit of capacitance is the farad, and we get $C = Q/V$, where C is in farads, Q is in coulombs and V in volts.

The farad is a rather large unit, so that we employ the microfarad = 10^{-6} of a farad or 1 picofarad = 10^{-12} of a farad.

CAPACITORS

The capacity of a body is increased by its proximity to earth or to another body and the combination of the two is termed a capacitor. So long as there is a potential difference between the two there is a capacitor action which is affected by the dielectric constant of the material in between the two bodies.

Flat Plate Capacitor.—Artificial capacitors are usually

CAPACITORS

Fig. I.   PLATE CAPACITOR

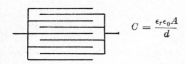

$$C = \frac{\epsilon_r \epsilon_0 A}{d}$$

Fig. 2.   CONCENTRIC CAPACITOR

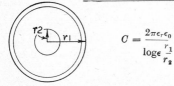

$$C = \frac{2\pi \epsilon_r \epsilon_0}{\log_\epsilon \frac{r_1}{r_2}}$$

Fig. 3.   CAPACITORS IN SERIES

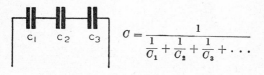

$$C = \frac{1}{\frac{1}{C_1} + \frac{1}{C_2} + \frac{1}{C_3} + \dots}$$

Fig. 4.   CAPACITORS IN PARALLEL

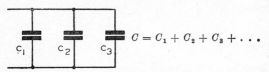

$$C = C_1 + C_2 + C_3 + \dots$$

made up of metal plates with paper or other materials as a dielectric. The rating of a plate capacitor is found from

$$C = \epsilon_r \epsilon_0 A/d \text{ farads}$$

where A is the area of each plate and d the thickness of the dielectric. For the multi-plate type we must multiply by the number of actual capacitors there are in parallel.

Concentric Capacitor.—With electric cables we get what is equivalent to a concentric capacitor with the outer conductor or casing of radius r_1 m. and the inner conductor of radius r_1 m. If now the dielectric has a constant of ϵ_r, the capacity will be (for 1 metre length)

$$C = \frac{2\pi\epsilon_r\epsilon_0}{\log_\epsilon \dfrac{r_1}{r_2}} \text{ farads per metre} = \frac{0 \cdot 039\epsilon_r}{\log_{10} \dfrac{r_1}{r_2}} \text{ microfarads per mile.}$$

Values of ϵ_r for Different Materials

Air	1
Paper, Pressboard	2
Cotton tape (rubbered) . . .	2
Empire cloth	2
Paper (oiled)	2
Shellac	3
Bakelite	6
Paraffin-wax	3
Mica	7
Porcelain	7
Glass	7
Marble	8
Rubber	2·5
Ebonite	2·5
Gutta-percha	4
Polyethylene	2·3

THE MAGNETIC CIRCUIT

Permanent Magnets.—These are now generally made from cobalt steel. The cobalt content varies from 3 per cent. to 35 per cent. Nickel-aluminium steels are also used and have the advantage that they are lighter in weight than cobalt steels (see p. 19).

Electro-magnets.—Magnetism is supposed to take the form of *lines of force* which flow round the magnetic circuit. This circuit may be a complete path of iron or may consist of an iron path with one or more air-gaps. The transformer is an example of the former and a dynamo the latter.

The lines of force are proportional to the *magneto-motive-force* of the electric circuit and this is given by

$$\text{M.M.F.} = \frac{IN}{10} \text{ ampere turns}$$

where I is the current in amperes and N the number of turns in the coil or coils. This m.m.f. is similar in many respects to the e.m.f. of an electric circuit and in the place of the resistance we have the *reluctance* which may be termed the resistance of the magnetic circuit to the passage of the lines of force. The reluctance is found from

$$\text{Reluctance} = S = \frac{l}{A \mu_r \mu_0} \text{ ampere turns/Weber}$$

where l is the length of the magnetic circuit in centimetres, A is the area of cross-section of the magnetic circuit and $\mu_r \mu_0$ is the permeability of the material. The permeability is a property of the actual magnetic circuit and not only varies with the material in the circuit but with the number of lines of force actually induced in the material if that material is iron.

The actual flux induced in any circuit is proportional to the ratio $\dfrac{\text{M.M.F.}}{\text{reluctance}}$ and so we get

$$\text{Total flux} = \Phi = \frac{\text{M.M.F.}}{S}.$$

The relative permeability μ_r is always given as the ratio of the number of lines of force induced in a circuit of any material compared with the number of lines induced in air for the same conditions. The permeability of air is taken as unity and so permeability can be taken as the magnetic conductivity compared with air.

Taking the formula for total flux given above, we can combine this by substituting values for m.m.f. and S, giving

$$\text{Total flux} = \varPhi = \frac{\mu_r \mu_0 INA}{10l} \text{ Webers.}$$

Having obtained the total flux, we can obtain the *flux density* or number of lines per square centimetre of cross-section as follows :

$$\text{Flux density} = \mathrm{B} = \frac{\varPhi}{A}$$

Where there is an air-gap it will be found that there is a certain amount of magnetic leakage and the actual flux in the air-gap will be smaller than that in the iron. The ratio between these two is given by the leakage coefficient which

$$= \frac{\text{flux in iron}}{\text{flux in air-gap}}$$

Ampere-turns per Centimetre.—In order to deal with complex magnetic circuits such as dynamos, motors, etc., it is more convenient to take the various sections of the magnetic circuit separately, and for this purpose it is useful to have the ampere-turns required per centimetre to give a fixed flux density. Taking our complete formula above for total flux, we get

$$B = \frac{\varPhi}{A} = \mu_r \mu_0 \frac{IN}{10l} = \mu_r \mu_0 H$$

so that the permeability and flux density are linked by the expression $\dfrac{IN}{10l} = H$ which is called the *magnetizing force* and it will be seen that this is equal to the ampere-turns per unit length (i.e. metre).

The relation between B and H is usually given by means of a B–H curve (Fig. 2, page 13), but by using a different scale the actual value of ampere-turns per centimetre required can be read off. This scale is also shown in the diagram.

ELECTRICAL MATERIALS

COPPER AND ITS ALLOYS

Copper.—The standard value of the resistivity of annealed high conductivity copper has been fixed at 0·017241 ohm./sq. mm per metre at 20° C, and material having this resistivity is said to have a conductivity of 100 per cent I.A.C.S. (International Annealed Copper Standard). Only silver with 106 per cent I.A.C.S. has a greater conductivity, but its high price and other factors preclude its general use, whereas the conductivity of aluminium is only 62 per cent I.A.C.S.

The electrical resistance of copper, as of all other pure metals, varies with the temperature. This variation is sufficient to reduce the conductivity of h.c. copper at 100° C to about 76 per cent of its value at 20° C.

The resistance $$R_{t'} = R_t[1 + \alpha_t(t' - t)]$$

where α_t is the constant mass temperature coefficient of resistance of copper at the reference $t°$ C. For a reference temperature of 0° C the formula becomes

$$R_t = R_0(1 + \alpha_0 t)$$

Although resistance may be regarded for all practical purposes as a linear function of temperature, the value of the temperature coefficient is not constant but is dependent upon, and varies with, the reference temperature according to the law

$$\alpha_t = \frac{1}{\dfrac{1}{\alpha_0} + t} = \frac{1}{234\cdot45 + t}$$

Thus the constant mass temperature coefficient of copper referred to a basic temperature of 0° C is

$$\alpha_0 = \frac{1}{234\cdot45} = 0\cdot004265 \text{ per ° C}$$

At 20° C the value of the constant mass temperature coefficient of resistance is

$$\alpha_{20} = \frac{1}{234\cdot45 + 20} = 0\cdot00393 \text{ per ° C}$$

which is the value adopted by the I.E.C.

Multiplier constants and their reciprocals, correlating the resistance of copper at a standard temperature, with the resistance at other temperatures, may be obtained from tables which are included in B.S. 7, 125, 128, 1432–1434.

Uses.—Most uses of h.c. copper call for it to be in either the fully annealed or the hard-drawn state, depending on the properties required for the items under manufacture. Hard-drawn copper has up to double the tensile strength of annealed copper and a conductivity approximately 3 per cent lower. Insulated cables, therefore, normally contain annealed copper, whereas overhead lines employ hard-drawn conductors.

The busbars used for many heavy-current conductors of relatively short length are usually made of hard-drawn copper. Copper busbars are available in a variety of shapes from the more conventional flat bar, rod and tube, to the so-called structural sections, channels, angles and tees.

Other special copper sections are used for rod-type earth electrodes and shaped switchgear contacts, while hollow copper conductors permit the water cooling of generator stator windings and result in very much higher power output.

Many commutators are made with ordinary high conductivity copper segments, but where the temperatures involved in the manufacture of the armature are such that an increased resistance to softening is desirable, silver-bearing copper (0·1 per cent silver) is employed—this small quantity of silver having virtually no effect upon conductivity. Silver-bearing copper also has improved resistance to creep, and for this reason it is used as the conductor material in the rotors of large alternators which now incorporate hollow conductors to facilitate hydrogen cooling.

However, most machines, both static and rotating, employ ordinary high-conductivity copper as the conductor material, an example of one of the few exceptions being the squirrel-cage induction motor, for some designs of which it is an advantage to have additional resistance in the rotor circuit to give increased starting torque. In such cases it is usual to obtain the lower conductivity required by employing either a copper alloy or one of the grades of copper not classed as high-conductivity material.

Copper conductors for machine windings are available with very many different forms of insulation including paper, glass, silicone and various types of enamel. Improvements in insulation now make it possible for machines to operate at temperatures around 200° C and for elevated temperature applications the designer can utilize silver- or nickel-plated copper conductors.

Sintered Alnico.—The techniques of powdered metallurgy have been applied to Alnico and it is possible to produce sintered permanent magnets which have approximately 10 per cent poorer remanence and energy than cast magnets. More

PROPERTIES OF ANISOTROPIC MATERIALS

Material.	Coercive Force. Oersted.	Remanence. Gauss, 10^3	(B.H.) max. gauss oersteds $\times 10^6$.	Density gm/cm^3
Tungsten Steel . .	65	10·5	0·30	8·1
Chromium Steel . .	70	9·8	0·285	7·8
Cobalt Steel, 3% Co .	130	7·2	0·35	7·7
,, ,, 6% Co .	145	7·5	0·4	7·8
,, ,, 9% Co .	160	7·8	0·50	7·8
,, ,, 15% Co .	180	8·2	0·62	7·9
,, ,, 35% Co .	250	9·0	0·95	8·1
Compressed powdered metal	410	8·6	1·6	4·0
Nickel, Aluminium Iron —Alni . .	500	6·0	1·3	7·0
,, Aluminium Cobalt Iron— Alnico I, II, III . . .	620/500	6·5/8	1·70	7·4
,, but Anisotropic —Alcomax III: Prepared axis . .	650	12·2	4·75	7·3
Hycomax I (High Coercive Alcomax): Prepared axis. . .	830	9	3·20	
Ticonal GX	720	13·5	7·5	7·3

precise shapes are possible when using this method of production and it is economical for the production of large quantities of small magnets.

Anisotropic Materials.—The Permanent Magnet Association discovered in 1938 that certain alloys when heat-treated in a strong magnetic field become anisotropic, i.e. they develop extremely high properties in the direction of the field at the expense of properties in other directions. This discovery has led to the development of extremely powerful magnets, of which Alcomax II and Hycomax are outstanding examples. The Table above shows the characteristics of the various materials now available for the manufacture of permanent magnets.

Material for Laminations.—Following the development of silicon iron as a soft magnetic material, hot rolled silicon steel sheet was used exclusively for laminated magnetic cores. The hot rolled sheet has now been superseded by cold reduced strip with silicon contents ranging from trace amounts to a little above 3 per cent. As the proportion of silicon increases, the electrical losses decrease and the saturation induction falls progressively to a figure of about 20 000 gauss for a steel containing 3 per cent of silicon.

Silicon steel strip such as B.S. 601 grades 253 and 216, is used for general purpose industrial motors while intermediate grades, 187 or 170, are used where lower power losses are required. These four grades have silicon contents in the range 0·5 to 2·5 per cent and are produced in standard thicknesses of 0·020 and 0·025 in. They can be obtained in the fully annealed or semi-processed condition.

Cold reduced steels with controlled composition, but with little or no silicon, are becoming widely used for producing small- to medium-sized electric motors. These grades, supplied in the semi-processed condition, have controlled hardness and surface characteristics to improve stamping performance. The laminations are annealed by the customer after stamping.

Grain-oriented (anisotropic) silicon steel, e.g. Unisil, Alphasil, is the material used almost exclusively for power and distribution transformers. Standard grades are to B.S. 601, Part 2.

Nickel Iron Alloy.—Nickel iron alloy containing about 25 per cent. of nickel is practically non-magnetic, but with increased nickel content and suitable heat treatment some remarkably high permeability materials have been obtained. These are particularly suitable for high-frequency applications.

Alloys in this group include Rhometal, Permalloy D, Radiometal, Permalloy B, Hipernik and Mumetal. The characteristics of these materials are given in the Table on page 20.

Supermalloy.—By adding 5 per cent. molybdenum to a high nickel content alloy (79 per cent. nickel, 15 per cent. iron) a material having extremely high initial permeability is obtained. The resulting alloy which is known as Supermalloy has a maximum permeability of approximately one million after suitable heat treatment.

Materials for Heating Elements.—The most usual material for the resistance wires which are used in making the elements of electric fires and heating appliances is an 18/20 nickel chromium alloy containing small quantities of carbon, silicon and iron. A rather different type of heating element which should be mentioned is that used in infra-red space heating equipment. The heating element is surrounded by a quartz tube giving heat in the 3 micron wave band.

Several other heat-resisting alloys have been developed, e.g. a heat-resisting alloy consisting of 65 per cent. nickel, 15 per cent. chromium, 20 per cent. iron, an unspecified alloy consisting of chromium, iron and aluminium for use as furnace elements. These alloys all have a specific resistance of about 110 microhms per cm. cube, so that their electrical properties to not impose any limitations on their application except that the temperature coefficient for nickel-chromium is less than for nickel-chromium-irons.

The nickel-chromium iron alloy is particularly suitable for use at the lower temperatures, e.g. for domestic utensils, whilst the nickel-chrome alloys have greater possibilities for heat-treatment furnaces and similar applications at a higher temperature range.

SUPERCONDUCTIVITY

SUPERCONDUCTIVITY is a term which has been adopted to signify the absence of electrical resistance in a given material. There are of course no materials which possess this property at the ordinary working temperatures, but it has been discovered that certain metals can be given the property of zero resistivity, or superconductivity, providing the temperature is reduced sufficiently.

In order to obtain these very low temperatures, it is necessary to immerse these materials in liquid hydrogen or liquid helium, and, therefore, the practical uses have been limited. Some scientific applications are, however, already being found, e.g. as sensitive detectors of heat radiation.

An important point to remember is that when a material is reduced to its zero resistance temperature, it becomes superconducting both to a.c. and d.c., providing the frequency of the former is below the megacycle range.

This fact is being made use of in " Crowe cell " memory devices in computers which store information in the form of electric currents circulating round and round indefinitely until needed. Crowe cells developed at the Royal Radar Establishment could release their information in 10^{-8} secs, 100 times faster than existing devices.

One manufacturer has made use of the phenomena of superconductivity in a transformer, the windings of which are kept at a very low temperature, thus reducing losses.

ELECTRONICS AND
SEMI-CONDUCTORS

During the last five years great advances have been made in the field of " light " current engineering particularly in the use of semi-conductors. Whereas valves and transistors were the province of the electronics engineer, the development from these to the silicon-controlled rectifier (now known as the thyristor) has caused a bridge to be built between the light and heavy current electrical engineer.

The main cause for this is that thyristors have reached a stage of being able to handle currents of up to 150 A (some even claim higher ratings), at 1 500 V, and the difficulties associated with operating them in series and parallel have been largely overcome. There is, therefore, a growing field of applications for the thyristor of which the power engineer must be aware.

In order to understand the operation of thyristors it is necessary to first discuss the principles of operation of the valve, including the function of the grid, for this was the forerunner of the present semi-conductor rectifier systems. Transistors and mercury-arc rectifiers are also both closely allied to the thyristor, the former in particular, and so some space is devoted in this chapter to discussing its mode of operation. The mercury-arc rectifier is described on page 132.

As far as the power engineer is concerned the applications of these sophisticated devices are more important than the theory of their operation, and it is this side which will be covered most fully. It is necessary, however, to describe the construction and operation of both the transistor and thyristor to appreciate some of the difficulties associated with their applications.

Thyratron.—The original thyratron was a triode valve containing a small amount of mercury vapour. The terms : grid-controlled rectifier and gas-filled relay, are alternative names for variations on the original thyratron construction. Argon, hydrogen, and other inert gases may be used instead of mercury vapour. In a vacuum triode the anode current varies according to the potential applied to the grid of the valve. In a gas-filled triode the grid potential can turn the anode current on, but thereafter is powerless to stop or modify its flow. Commercially available thyratrons can handle mean anode currents of the order of 0·5 to 33 amperes

of the n–p–n section and I_{co_2} is the collector to base leakage of the p–n–p section, then

for the p–n–p section : $I_{c_1} = h_{fe_1}(I_{c_2} + I_{co_1}) + I_{co_1}$
for the n–p–n section : $I_{c_2} = h_{fe_2}(I_{c_1} + I_{co_2}) + I_{co_2}$

and the total anode-to-cathode current $I_a = (I_{c_1} + I_{c_2})$

from which $I_a = \dfrac{(1 + h_{fe_1})(1 + h_{fe_2})(I_{co_1} + I_{co_2})}{1 - (h_{fe_1})(h_{fe_2})}$

With a proper bias applied, i.e. positive anode to cathode voltage, the structure is said to be in the forward blocking or high impedance " off " state. The switch to the low impedance " on " state is initiated simply by raising the loop gain G to unity. As this occurs the circuit starts to regenerate, each transistor driving its mate to saturation. Once in saturation all junctions assume a forward bias, and the total potential drop across the device approximates to that of a single junction. Anode current is then only limited by the external circuit.

To turn off the thyristor in a minimum time it is necessary to apply a reverse voltage and under this condition the holes and electrons in the vicinity of the two end junctions will diffuse in these junctions and result in a reverse current in the external circuit. The voltage across the thyristor will remain at about 0·7 V positive as long as an appreciable reverse current flows. After the holes and electrons in the vicinity of the two end junctions have been removed, the reverse current will cease and the junction will assume a blocking state. The turn-off time is usually of the order of 10 to 15 microseconds. The fundamental difference between the transistor and thyristor is that with the former conduction can be stopped at any point in the cycle because the current gain is less than unity. This is not so for the thyristor, conduction only stopping at a current zero.

Thyristor Applications

Excitation of Synchronous Motors.—Most specifications for synchronous motors state that they must be capable of withstanding a gradually applied momentary overload torque without losing synchronism. In B.S. 2613 this is given as 1·5 times full load for a period of 15 seconds at normal rated voltage for synchronous motors and 1·35 times full load for synchronous induction motors.

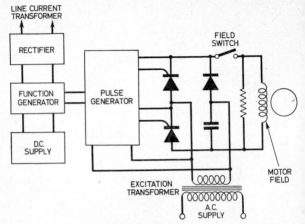

FIG. 11.—Simple Compensated Excitation Circuit.

In the past this has been met by using a larger frame size than necessary to meet full-load torque requirements, the torque being proportional to the product of the a.c. supply voltage and the d.c. field produced by the excitation current.

With thyristor control of excitation current it is possible to use a smaller frame size for a given horsepower rating and arrange to boost the excitation by means of a controller to avoid loss of synchronism under torque overload conditions.

The excitation current of a synchronous motor may be controlled by supplying the motor field winding from a static thyristor bridge, using the motor supply current to control the firing angle, Fig. 11. A pulse generator varies the firing angle of the thyristors in proportion to a d.c. control signal from a diode function generator. Variable elements in the function generator enable a reasonable approximation to be made to any of a wide range of compensating characteristics.

When the motor operates asynchronously, i.e. during starting, a high e.m.f. is induced in the field winding, and the resulting voltage appearing across the bridge must be limited to prevent the destruction of the bridge elements. This may be done by using a shunt resistor connected as shown. Where more exacting requirements have to be met, current feedback can be applied to eliminate effects of non-linearity in the pulse generator and rectifier bridge and it will also improve the response of the system to sudden changes of load. Automatic synchronizing is possible without relays by incorporating a slip-frequency sensing circuit to control the gate which supplies the control signal to the pulse generator.

Variable Frequency Supply.—It is possible to use a cycloconverter to control the speed of an induction motor. The cycloconverter is a rectifier device first developed in the 1930's but with the improved control characteristics of thyristors and better circuit techniques, a continuously variable output frequency is possible.

Fig. 12 illustrates the process of conversion for 15 c/s output from 50 c/s supply. During the conduction cycle starting at point a the output voltage reaches a maximum since there is no firing delay. At point b commutation from phase two to phase three is slightly delayed and commutation is further delayed at point c.

At time e the firing delay is such that the mean output voltage is only just possible. In the diagram the low-frequency load power factor is 0·6 lagging so that although the mean load voltage crosses the axis at X the current remains positive until Y. Consequently the rectifiers which conduct at instants f, g and h are giving positive load current and negative voltage, that is inverting. From i the system behaves as a controlled rectifier using the negative group of thyristors, d, e and f until the mean output voltage becomes positive when an inversion period starts again.

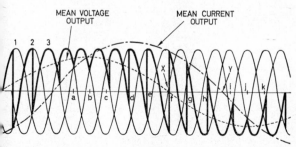

MEAN VOLTAGE OUTPUT   MEAN CURRENT OUTPUT

Fig. 12.—Synthesis of 15 c/s from 50 c/s (load power factor 0·6 lagging).

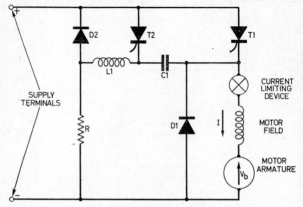

Fig. 13.—Basic circuit for Motoring.

Controlling a d.c. Motor.—The basic circuit is shown in Fig. 13, the supply being applied to the motor by firing $T1$. At standstill the current rises rapidly to a value controlled by the circuit resistance and at a rate controlled by the inductance of the motor.

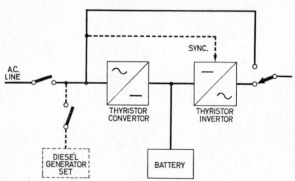

Fig. 14.—Static Standby Power System.

ELECTRICAL INSULATING MATERIALS

THE chief materials used in the insulation of electrical equipment are grouped into the following recognized classes :

Class Y insulation consists of materials or combinations of materials such as cotton, silk and paper without impregnation. Other materials or combinations of materials may be included in this class if by experience or tests they can be shown to be capable of operation at the Class Y temperature.

Class A insulation consists of materials such as cotton, silk and paper when suitably impregnated or coated or when immersed in a dielectric liquid such as oil. Other materials or combinations of materials may be included in this class if by experience or tests they can be shown to be capable of operation at the Class A temperature.

Class E insulation consists of materials or combinations of materials which by experience or tests can be shown to be capable of operation at the Class E temperature (materials possessing a degree of thermal stability allowing them to be operated at 15° C higher than Class A materials). Such materials are synthetic-resin impregnated and enamelled wire not associated with fibrous materials such as cotton, silk or paper.

Class B insulation consists of materials or combinations of materials such as mica, glass fibre, asbestos, etc., with suitable bonding, impregnating or coating substances. Bare coils come in this category. Other materials or combinations of materials, not necessarily inorganic, may be included in this class, if by experience or tests they can be shown to be capable of operation at the Class B temperature.

Class F insulation consists of materials or combinations of materials such as mica, glass fibre, asbestos, etc., with suitable bonding, impregnating or coating substances, as well as other materials or combinations of materials, not necessarily inorganic, which by experience or tests can be shown to be capable of operation at the Class F temperature (materials possessing a degree of thermal stability allowing them to be operated at 25° C higher than Class B materials).

Class H insulation consists of materials such as silicone elastomer and combinations of materials such as mica, glass fibre, asbestos, etc., with suitable bonding, impregnated or coating substances such as appropriate silicone resins. Other materials or combinations of materials may be included in this class if by experience or tests they can be shown to be capable of operation at the Class H temperature.

Class C insulation consists of materials or combinations of materials such as mica, porcelain, glass, quartz and asbestos with or without an inorganic binder. Other materials may be included in this class, if by experience or tests they can be shown to be capable of operation at temperatures above the Class H limit. Specific materials or combinations of materials in this class will have a temperature limit which is dependent upon their physical, chemical and electrical properties.

In each class, a proportion of materials of a lower temperature class may be included for structural purposes only, provided that adequate electrical and mechanical properties are maintained during the application of the maximum permitted temperature.

An insulating material is considered to be " suitably impregnated when a suitable substance such as varnish penetrates the interstices between fibres, films, etc., to a sufficient degree adequately to bond components of the insulation structure and to provide a surface film which adequately excludes moisture, dirt and other contaminants.

For some applications, compounds and resins without solvents are used which substantially displace all the air in the interstices. In other applications, varnishes or other materials containing solvents are used which provide reasonably continuous surface films and partial filling of the interstices with some degree of bonding between components of the insulation structure.

Temperature Limits.—The recognized classes of insulating materials and the temperatures assigned to them are as follows :

Class.	Temperature.
Y (formerly O)	90° C
A	105° C
E	120° C
B	130° C
F	155° C
H	180° C
C	above 180° C

Properties.—The following notes give briefly the chief points to be borne in mind when considering the suitability of any material for a particular duty.

Specific Gravity is of importance for varnishes, oils and other liquids. The density of solid insulations varies widely, e.g. from 0·6 for certain papers to 3·0 for mica. In a few cases it indicates the relative quality of a material, e.g. vulcanized fibre and pressboard.

Moisture Absorption usually causes serious depreciation of electrical properties, particularly in oils and fibrous materials. Swelling, warping, corrosion and other effects often result from absorption of moisture. Under severe conditions of humidity, such as occur in mines and in tropical climates, moisture sometimes causes serious deterioration.

Thermal Effects very often seriously influence the choice and application of insulating materials, the principal features being : melting-point (e.g. of waxes) ; softening or plastic yield temperature ; ageing due to heat, and the maximum temperature which a material will withstand without serious deterioration of essential properties ; flash point or ignitibility ; resistance to electric arcs ; liability to carbonize (or " track ") ; ability to self-extinguish if ignited ; specific heat ; thermal resistivity ; and certain other thermal properties such as coefficient of expansion and freezing-point.

Mechanical Properties.—The usual mechanical properties of solid materials are of varying significance in the case of those required for insulating purposes, *tensile* strength, *transverse* strength, *shearing* strength and *compressive* strength often being specified. Owing, however, to the relative degree of inelasticity of most solid insulations, and the fact that many are quite brittle, it is frequently necessary to pay attention to such features as *compressibility, deformation under bending* stresses, *impact* strength and *extensibility, tearing* strength, *machinability* and ability to fold without damage.

Resistivity and Insulation Resistance.—In the case of insulating material it is generally manifest in two forms (*a*) volume resistivity (or specific resistance) and (*b*) surface resistivity.

Electric Strength (or Dielectric Strength) is the property of an insulating material which enables it to withstand electric stress without injury. It is usually expressed in terms of the minimum electric stress (i.e. potential difference per unit distance) which will cause failure or " breakdown " of the dielectric under certain specified conditions.

Surface Breakdown and Flash-over.—When a high-voltage stress is applied to conductors separated only by air and the stress is increased, breakdown of the intermediate air will take place when a certain stress is attained, being accompanied by the passage of a spark from one conductor to the other.

Permittivity (Specific Inductive Capacity).—Permittivity is defined as the ratio of the electric flux density produced in the material to that produced in free space by the same electric force, and is expressed as the ratio of the capacitance of a

59

ELECTRICAL CHARACTERISTICS OF TYPICAL INSULATING MATERIALS AT 20° C APPROX

Material	Volume Resistivity Ω/cm	Permittivity (S.I.C.)	Power Factor 50 c/s
Impregnated paper	10^{17}	2·5–3·5	0·001 7–0·003 5
Insulating oil*—low viscosity, cable, capacitor	10^{7}	2·3	0·000 01
—high viscosity			
(i) cable 37% aromatics	$3·2 \times 10^{15}$	2·31	0·000 01
(ii) cable 22% aromatics	$2·4 \times 10^{15}$	2·31	0·000 05
(iii) cable 30% polyisobutylene	10^{17}	2·34	0·000 03
Chlorinated diphenyls (Aroclor 1242†)	10^{8}–10^{8}	6·0	0·000 6
Rubbers: Pure unvulcanised	10^{14}–10^{16}	2·4	0·002 8 at 100 c/s
Vulcanized natural . .	10^{14}–10^{16}	2·94	0·004 8 at 100 c/s
Plastics		see page 66.	
Silicones: Fluid MS 200‡ at 1 000 c/s	—	2·75	0·000 4
[Silastomer‡ rubber grade 6–128	—	2·85	0·000 3**
Resin coating varnish MS 994‡	—	2·8	0·001 5
Impregnating varnish MS 997‡	—	3·06	0·006
Glass laminates . . .	5×10^{11}		0·002**
Steatite	10^{8}–10^{9}	6·3	0·001 5
Glass	10^{12}–10^{20}	3·7–10	0·004–0·007**
Mica, clear ruby . . .	10^{7}–10^{11}	5·4	0·25
Fibreglass, 65 per cent r.h. .	10^{9}||	5·0	0·25

* At 100 c/s.
† Monsanto Chemicals.
‡ Midland Silicones.
** at 10^{6} c/s.
†† Ω/cm³.
|| Information extracted mainly from Modern Dielectric Materials by J. B. Birks.

dehyde at temperatures between 90° C to 100° C, either with or without a catalyser, in a digester equipped for refluxing usually with arrangements for removal of water. Ammonia, soda or other alkaline catalysts are generally employed, and sometimes acid catalysts are used. The final polymerizing or " curing " time of the resin, which vitally affects its utility, is varied as desired by the manufacturing process, some resins curing in a few seconds, say, at 150° C and others requiring an hour or more to effect complete curing. The resins are sometimes in a semi-liquid form but more usually are solids with softening points ranging from 60° C to 100° C.

The main disadvantages of PF plastics are restriction to dark-brownish colours and tracking by flashover of surface char.

Urea-Formaldehyde (UF) and Melamine-Formaldehyde (MF).—These are aminoplastics and both are more expensive than phenolics. They are available in pale, translucent colours, including white, and are non-tracking. The more expensive melamines have better moisture resistance and superior mechanical properties than the phenolics although their uses are similar. They are particularly suitable where cost is subservient to the appearance and non-tracking requirements.

Urea formaldehyde resins are produced from urea or thiourea reacted with formaldehyde. If the condensation process is only partially carried out, useful water-soluble adhesives are obtained which can be set hard after application to joints by means of addition of suitable hardeners. They are used for glueing plywood and similar materials by cold pressing, or by hot pressing when improved water resistance is required.

Melamine-formaldehyde resins are similar to the urea type and are produced by the reaction of melamine (an amino derivative of cyanide) with formaldehyde.

Polyester (PR), and Alkyd (AK).—The group known as alkydes are mainly used in paints and varnishes, but when moulded the materials are non-tracking and have superior heat resistance to UF, MF, and PF, both wet and dry. They are the condensation products of polybasic acids (e.g. phtalic and tartaric acids) with polyhydric alcohols (e.g. glycerol and glycol).

The main use of polyester resins is in combination with glass or asbestos fibres. These resins can cure with a catalyst at ambient temperature and with any light (contact) pressures, thus making possible large, strong structures at low capital

PROPERTIES OF THERMOPLASTICS SYNTHETIC RESINS

Property.	Polytetrafluorethylene.	Polyethylene (Low Density).	Polystyrene (General Purpose).	Acrylics.	Polamide (Nylon 6).	Vinyl Chloride (Rigid).
Specific Gravity at 20° C	2·1–2·3	0·913–0·925	1·04–1·11	1·17–1·20	1–13	1·38–1·4
Softening Point, ° C	> 300	85–87	82–103	80–98	215–220	82
Water Absorption, %	0·00	<0·015	0·03–0·4	0·3–0·4	1·9–3·3	0·05
Volume Resistivity, ohms/cm	10^{19}	$>10^{16}$	$>10^{18}$	$>10^{14}$	$10^{12}-10^{15}$	$10^{13}-10^{16}$
Electric Strength, v./mil.	400–500	>800	500–700	450–550	440–510	425
Dielectric Constant at 10^{6} c/s	2·0	2·25–2·35	2·4–3·1	2·8–3·2	3–5	3·0
Dissipation (Power) Factor at 10^{6} c/s (tan δ)	5×10^{-3}	$<2 \times 10^{-4}$	0·0001–0·005	0·02–0·04	0·02–0·13	0·006
Tensile Strength, lb/in²	2 500–3 500	1 000–2 300	5 000–12 000	7 000–11 000	10 200–12 000	8 500
Modulus of Elasticity, lb/in² × 10^{-5}	0·38–0·65	0·17–0·35	4–6	4–5	1·5–3·6	3·5–6·0
Flexural Strength, lb/in²	1 600	No fracture	12 000–17 000	13 000–17 000	8 000–16 000	13 500
Izod Impact Strength, ft-lb/in	2·5–4·0	>16	0·2–0·5	0·3–0·5	1·0–3·6	0·8
Elongation, %	250–350	400–600	1·0–2·5	3–10	90–320	2–40
Thermal Conductivity, cal/sec/cm²/° C/cm × 10^{-4}	6·0	8·0	2·4–3·3	4–6	—	3·5

Acknowledgement is made to Shell Booklet: "Properties of Plastics."

PROPERTIES OF TYPICAL THERMOSETTING RESINS

Property.	Phenol-Formaldehyde (Woodflour/Cotton Flock Filled).	Urea Formaldehyde.	Melamine (α-Cellulose Filled).	Epoxide Resin Araldite CT200* (Filled System)	Polyester Resin (Unfilled).
Specific Gravity at 20° C	1·32–1·45	1·47–1·52	1·47–1·52	1·75	1·22
Heat Distortion Temperature, ° F	260–340	270–280	400	221–240	—
Water Absorption, %	0·3–1·0	0·4–0·8	0·1–0·6	0·25–0·3	0·15
Volume Resistivity, ohms/cm³	10^9–10^{13}	10^{12}–10^{13}	10^{12}–10^{14}	$>10^{15}$	10^{13}
Electric Strength, v/mil	200–425	300–400	300–400	450–525	550
Dielectric Constant at 10^6 c/s	4·0–7·0	6·4–6·9	7·2–8·2	4·0–4·2†	3·2
Dissipation (Power) Factor at 10^6 c/s (tan δ)	4·5–5·0	0·028–0·032	0·027–0·045	0·015–0·025†	0·019
Tensile Strength, lb/in²	6 500–8 500	6 000–13 000	7 000–13 000	9 000–12 000	9 000
Modulus of Elasticity, lb/in² $\times 10^{-5}$	8–12	15	13	11–13	5
Flexural Strength, lb/in²	8 000–12 000	10 000–16 000	10 000–16 000	19 000–20 000	9 000–13 000
Izod Impact Strength, ft-lb/in	0·24–0·6	0·25–0·35	0·24–0·36	—	0·4
Elongation, %	0·4–0·8	0·5–1·0	0·6–0·9	—	—
Thermal Conductivity, cal/sec/cm²/° C/cm $\times 10^{-4}$	4·7	7–10	0·6–0·9	14–16	5·0

Acknowledgement is made to Shell Booklet: " Properties of Plastics."

* Ciba Trade Name.

† at 1 kc/s.

cost. As well as sheets for insulation, glass-fibre polyester or reinforced plastics (RP) mouldings are used for covers and guards, line-operating poles, insulated ladders and many other applications where large, strong, complex-shaped insulated components are required.

Epoxide Resins (EP).—These have similar but superior properties to PR, but are more expensive. They can be cast into large insulators, or used to encapsulate electronic components and circuits, and also for the insulation of rotor and stator windings. Adhesion qualities, including metal-to-metal, are outstanding.

Thermoplastics.—There are three main processing methods for the production of thermoplastics components namely : injection moulding, in which the hot plastics is forced into a cool mould ; extrusion, in which the hot material is forced through a profiled die to produce a length of material of constant section, including insulated and sheathed cable ; and thermoforming, in which hot sheet is formed into shapes, often aided by vacuum or compressed air.

Polyethylene, Polythene (PE).—The excellent dielectric properties of this material make it outstanding as an insulating medium in circuits where there are high-frequency currents. It is safe to say that polythene made radar a possibility. It is also possible to mould unbreakable plugs directly onto a cable end. It is made by subjecting ethylene to very high pressures and is a wax-like translucent product.

Polyterafluorethylene (PTFE).—Closely related to polythene, but with enhanced resistance to chemical attack at high temperatures, this material is used where aggressive environments justify its high cost. It is only affected by molten alkali metals and a few fluorine compounds at high temperature and pressure.

In addition it is a good electrical insulator, particularly so because it is non-tracking and incombustible. It is not wetted by water, which it does not absorb, and it has excellent weathering and ageing characteristics. It has a working temperature of over 250° C. In appearance it is ivory white, smooth and waxy to the touch.

Polyvinyl Chloride (PVC).—Unlike polythene, this material is self-extinguishing, and can be modified with plasticizers to give virtually any degree of flexibility. It is tough and abrasion-resistant, and its main electrical use is for cable insulation and sheathing and for non-metallic conduit. Oil resistance is good.

Vinyl chloride is obtained from the combination of acetylene

SOLAR POWER

Although it has been appreciated by the scientists for a very long time that solar energy represented a vast source of supply, very little has been done in the past to tap it. Within the last few years, however, interest has quickened and today there are many practical devices in operation.

The main component is the solar cell. This is a thin disc of pure silicon containing a minute quantity of boron (or similar substance) to give the silicon a negative potential. A layer of p-type material a few microns thick is diffused on to the upper surface of the disc and the ends lapped over the perimeter.

This portion is then enclosed in a containing case with a glass face, the top surface of the disc being filled with silicon grease to prevent loss by reflection.

As will be appreciated from the description, the arrangement broadly speaking is similar to that found in a transistor where electrons flowing from the n-plate to the " holes " of the p-plate constitute a current. In the solar cell, power is produced by this process at the barrier junction.

The overall efficiency of such an arrangement is of the order of 12 per cent, which although low, should be compared with the figure of 0·1 per cent for a photo-electric cell.

An indication of the performance of a typical solar cell is given by the following figures, which relate to a unit made by Hoffman Electronics Corporation of America. The power output in full sunlight (i.e. clear blue sky with normal atmosphere) is 44 mW for an area of 4·75 sq. cm representing an output of $9\frac{1}{4}$ mW per sq. cm. Open-circuit voltage is 0·55 V and the short-circuit current is 150 mA. The voltage for maximum power is 0·4 V with a current of 110 mA. Overall efficiency is 8·7 per cent.

The presence of moisture or carbon dioxide in the atmosphere has an adverse effect on the performance of a solar cell, so that too much vegetation should be avoided when considering an installation.

The resistance of a cell varies in an adverse manner to the amount of light received and this is a vital factor when considering the operation of a number of cells in parallel-series arrangement. If a foreign body obscured one cell it would have an adverse effect on the whole arrangement due to the increased resistance of this unit.

The solar cell finds applications as the power source for telephones in rural areas, for telephone repeaters, guided missiles and space-research vehicles.

TRANSMISSION AND DISTRIBUTION

Two-Wire D.C.—Referring to Fig. 1, the volt drop in each conductor $= IR$, therefore the total volt drop $= 2IR$. The voltage drop will therefore be given by $E - V = 2IR$. The power loss in each conductor $= I^2R$. Therefore total power loss $= 2I^2R$.

$$\text{Efficiency} = \frac{\text{output}}{\text{input}} = \frac{VI}{EI} = \frac{EI - 2I^2R}{EI}$$

$$= \frac{VI}{VI + 2I^2R}.$$

$$\text{Voltage regulation} = \frac{E - V}{V} = \frac{2IR}{V}.$$

Single-Phase A.C.—Referring to diagram in Fig. 2, the constants are shown as X and R, where X is the reactance of the conductor and R is its resistance (capacitance is neglected here).

Taking the power factor of the load as $\cos \phi$, the relation between the volts at the receiving end V, and the sending end E, will be given by

$$E = \sqrt{(V \cos \phi + 2IR)^2 + (V \sin \phi + 2IX)^2}.$$

The volt drop and regulation can be found from the values of E and V.

An approximate value for the volt drop per conductor is given by $IR \cos \phi + IX \sin \phi$. So that the total volt drop will be $2(IR \cos \phi + IX \sin \phi)$.

The power loss per line is I^2R giving a total power loss of $2I^2R$. The power factor at the supply end is found from

$$\tan \phi_1 = \frac{(V \sin \phi + 2IX)}{(V \cos \phi + 2IR)}$$

and the efficiency will be found by

$$\frac{VI \cos \phi}{VI \cos \phi + 2I^2R}.$$

Three-Phase A.C.—Neglecting capacitance, the line constants will be as shown in Fig. 3 and the following details refer to a balanced delta connected load.

Reactance and resistance drops per conductor will be IX and IR. But for three-phase reactance and resistance drops per phase will be $\sqrt{3}IX$ and $\sqrt{3}IR$. The relation between V and E will then be given by

$$E = \sqrt{(V \cos \phi + \sqrt{3}IR)^2 + (V \sin \phi + \sqrt{3}XI)^2}.$$

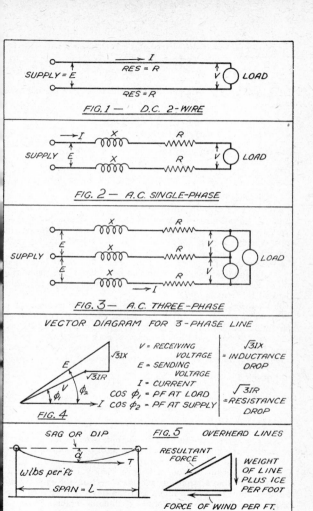

FIG.1 — D.C. 2-WIRE

FIG. 2 — A.C. SINGLE-PHASE

FIG. 3 — A.C. THREE-PHASE

VECTOR DIAGRAM FOR 3-PHASE LINE

V = RECEIVING VOLTAGE
E = SENDING VOLTAGE
I = CURRENT
$\cos \phi_1$ = PF AT LOAD
$\cos \phi_2$ = PF AT SUPPLY

$\sqrt{3} I x$ = INDUCTANCE DROP
$\sqrt{3} I R$ = RESISTANCE DROP

FIG. 4

FIG. 5 OVERHEAD LINES

SAG OR DIP

w lbs per ft
SPAN = L

RESULTANT FORCE
WEIGHT OF LINE PLUS ICE PER FOOT
FORCE OF WIND PER FT.

The power factor at the supply end can then be obtained from

$$\tan \phi_1 = \frac{(V \sin \phi + \sqrt{3} IX)}{(V \cos \phi + \sqrt{3} IR)}.$$

The loss in each line will be $I^2 R$, the total loss in this case being $3 I^2 R$. The efficiency can be found from

$$\frac{\sqrt{3} VI \cos \phi}{\sqrt{3} VI \cos \phi + 3 I^2 R}.$$

The voltage regulation of the line will be found from $\frac{E - V}{V}$.

The vector diagram for a three-phase circuit is shown in Fig. 4, and this can be used for single phase by omitting the $\sqrt{3}$ before the IR and IX.

Kelvin's Law.—In any transmission line it can be shown that the maximum economy is obtained when the annual capital cost of the line equals the cost of the energy loss in transmission during the year. This is known as Kelvin's Law and is used as a guide for determining the size which should be used for a transmission line. The result obtained by applying Kelvin's Law must be considered also from the point of view of volt drop, current-carrying capacity and mechanical construction.

The capital cost of a line is the cost (usually taken over a year) for the interest on the capital expended, plus depreciation and maintenance. Usually a figure of between 10 per cent and 20 per cent of the capital cost is taken to cover these items. The energy loss in the line during the year can only be estimated and the following equation can be used

$$\frac{eBs}{100} = \frac{m I^2 Rp \times 8760}{1000 \times 240}$$

where e = interest and depreciation in percentage per annum
B = cost per thousand yards of line per square inch of cross-section s in £
m = number of conductors
I = R.M.S. value of the current taken over a year
R = the resistance of one conductor per thousand yards
p = the cost in pence for energy per unit
s = section of line in square inches.

From the above equation the ideal section for any transmission line can be obtained and the nearest standard size larger should first be considered. Full consideration must be given to the other points mentioned above.

by the spring. If the voltage rises to a predetermined value the pull of this spring is overcome and the main contacts are broken. This action disconnects winding b of the relay, the effect of which is in opposition to winding a, so that the

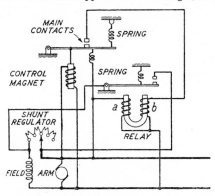

Fig. 6.—Connection of Tirrill Regulator for D.C. Generators.

relay accordingly opens its contacts, inserting the whole of the effective shunt regulator resistance into the field circuit. The resultant fall of generated voltage causes the control magnet to release and close the main contacts, which reconnect winding b of the relay, thus causing the relay contacts to reclose and short circuit the shunt regulator. The resulting rise of voltage causes the foregoing cycle of operations to be repeated and the process continues rapidly so as to maintain the regulated voltage within prescribed limits determined by the setting of the relay.

Electronic Voltage Regulators.—This type of regulator has been in use for a number of years for a.c. and d.c. generators and has proved to be both reliable and easily maintained. Very close regulation is possible (0·1 per cent for certain applications) and the regulator performs its function without any moving parts. (See Fig. 7.)

The line voltage is transformed to a suitable value, rectified, and applied to the " non-linear " bridge B. This bridge comprises two pairs of resistances, R_0 and R_N. The resistances of R_0 remain constant under all conditions. The resistances R_N are of the " non-linear " type. R_N and R_0 are so chosen that at the correct voltage across L_1 and L_2 they are equal to each other; hence the voltage across XY is zero; i.e. the bridge is balanced. If the line voltage is above its correct value, a rise of voltage occurs across the resistances R_N, and thus their value also rises. Since the resistances R_0 retain their original value, the line X is now negative with respect to Y. Similarly, if a drop in line voltage occurs, both resistances R_N fall in value and X becomes positive with respect to Y.

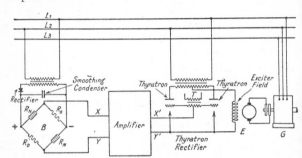

FIG. 7.—Simplified Diagram of Thyratron Voltage Regulator.

Such changes in voltage across X and Y are amplified in the single-stage amplifier, before passing to the grid circuit of the thyratrons, which are connected as a simple two-phase rectifier, the output of which supplies the field of the exciter E.

If the line voltage is high, the negative voltage impressed on the thyratron grid circuit in combination with the constant a.c. voltage fed in by the transformer T lowers the thyratron rectifier output to a low value. The exciter field is, therefore, weakened and thus a drop of exciter and main generator voltage occurs. The reverse action takes place if the line voltage is low.

Automatic Rheostat-Type Regulator.—The Brown-Boveri regulator employs a special rotary-type induction relay accurately adjusted to operate mechanically a special sector form of rheostat in the field circuit. Ingenious mechanism is introduced to cause the rheostat to overshoot and return more gradually, under the control of an adjustable electromagnet damping device, to that position which provides the correct voltage under the new conditions.

POWER FACTOR IMPROVEMENT

By Capacitors.—The kVA required for power factor correction will be found by reference to the vector diagram on page 127. The load current is represented by OI_L lagging by angle ϕ_1, such that $\cos \phi_1$ is the power factor of the load.

Assuming that it is desired to improve the power factor to $\cos \phi_2$ by means of capacitors, the resultant current must be represented by OI_R in Fig. 1. The method employed is the constant kW one.

To obtain this amount of correction the capacitor current of OI_C must equal $I_L - I_R$, and this value will be given by $OI_C = OI_L \sin \phi_1 - OI_R \sin \phi_2$.

The vector diagram is drawn for current, but is also applicable to kVA since the current is directly proportional to the kVA. Thus OI_L, OI_C and OI_R can be taken to represent the kVA of the load, the capacitor and the resultant kVA respectively.

In this case the initial conditions would be:

$$\cos \phi_1 = \frac{\text{kW}}{\text{kVA}_L}$$

$$\tan \phi_1 = \frac{\text{kVA}r_L}{\text{kW}}$$

$$\text{kVA}r_L = \text{kW} \tan \phi_1$$

The improved conditions would be:

$$\cos \phi_2 = \frac{\text{kW}}{\text{kVA}r_R}$$

$$\tan \phi_2 = \frac{\text{kVA}r_R}{\text{kW}}$$

$$\therefore \text{kVA}r_R = \text{kW} \tan \phi_2.$$

Capacitor kVAr required to improve power factor from $\cos \phi_1$ to $\cos \phi_2$

$$= (\text{kVA}r_L - \text{kVA}r_R)$$
$$= \text{kW}(\tan \phi_1 - \tan \phi_2).$$

Actual Capacity Required.—It may be necessary to transform capacitor kVA to microfarad capacity and the following relationship shows how this should be done.

Single Phase.—Current in capacitor is given by

$$I_C = 2\pi f C V$$
$$I_C = \text{current in amps.}$$
$$f = \text{frequency}$$

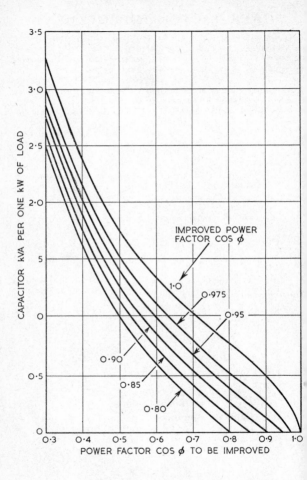

C = rating of capacitor in farads
V = voltage
(*Note.*—1 farad = 10^6 microfarads.)

Three Phase.—The total line current taken by three capacitors in delta is as shown in Fig. 3 and is given by

line current = $\sqrt{3}$ phase current in each capacitor.
Total line current = $\sqrt{3}(2\pi fCV)$.

WATTLESS AND POWER COMPONENTS FOR VARIOUS POWER FACTORS

Power Factor Cos ϕ.	Angle ϕ.	Per kVA.		Per kW.	
		Power.	Wattless.	kVA.	Wattless Component.
1·0	0	1·0	0	1·0	0
0·98	11·48	0·98	0·20	1·02	0·20
0·96	16·26	0·96	0·28	1·04	0·29
0·94	19·95	0·94	0·34	1·06	0·36
0·92	23·07	0·92	0·39	1·09	0·43
0·90	25·83	0·90	0·44	1·11	0·48
0·88	28·37	0·88	0·48	1·14	0·54
0·86	30·68	0·86	0·51	1·16	0·59
0·84	32·87	0·84	0·54	1·19	0·65
0·82	34·92	0·82	0·57	1·22	0·70
0·80	36·87	0·80	0·60	1·25	0·75
0·78	38·73	0·78	0·63	1·28	0·80
0·76	40·53	0·76	0·65	1·32	0·86
0·74	42·27	0·74	0·67	1·35	0·91
0·72	43·95	0·72	0·69	1·39	0·96
0·70	45·57	0·70	0·71	1·43	1·02
0·68	47·15	0·68	0·73	1·47	1·08
0·66	48·70	0·66	0·75	1·52	1·14
0·64	50·20	0·64	0·77	1·56	1·20
0·62	51·68	0·62	0·78	1·61	1·27
0·60	53·13	0·60	0·80	1·67	1·33
0·58	54·55	0·58	0·82	1·72	1·40
0·56	55·93	0·56	0·83	1·79	1·48
0·54	57·32	0·54	0·84	1·85	1·56
0·52	58·66	0·52	0·85	1·92	1·64
0·50	60	0·50	0·87	2·00	1·73

The kVA is $\sqrt{3}\ VI \times 10^3$ so that the kVA is given by

$$\text{kVA} = \frac{3(2\pi fCV^2)}{1000}.$$

The C used in the above formula is the rating of one of the three capacitors forming the delta and so the total rating is $3C$. This gives us the formula:

$$\text{Rating of each capacitor} = C = \frac{\text{kVA} \times 1000}{3(2\pi f.V^2)}$$

$$\therefore \text{Total rating} = 3C = \frac{\text{kVA} \times 1000}{2\pi f.V^2}.$$

Synchronous Motor Correction.—Referring to the diagram in Fig. 2 the current required for the synchronous motor cannot always be fixed by the desired amount of power factor correction, as in this case it is driving a load and the actual current will be fixed by the load on the synchronous motor and the power factor at which it is working.

It is impracticable to give formulae for working out these values as it is much better to start with the possible main load and the variable load which can be used for the synchronous motor.

Referring to the vector diagram, if values are taken either for currents as shown in the vector diagram or their proportionate kVA, their resultant current or kVA can be obtained as follows:

$$OI_R = \sqrt{(OI_L \cos\phi_1 + OI_M \cos\phi_2)^2 + (OI_L \sin\phi_1 - OI_M \sin\phi_2)^2}.$$

Resultant power factor can be obtained from

$$\tan\phi_3 = \frac{(OI_L \sin\phi_1 - OI_M \sin\phi_2)}{(OI_L \cos\phi_1 + OI_M \cos\phi_2)}.$$

If in any given case there is a fixed main load at a stated power factor plus a given kW load for the synchronous motor it is advisable to calculate the resultant power factor by working this out for various leading power factors for the synchronous motor.

It should be borne in mind that synchronous and synchronous induction motors will not work satisfactorily at a very low power factor. Values between 0·6 and 0·9 leading are usually taken for satisfactory results.

POWER FACTOR CORRECTION

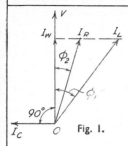

OI_L = LOAD CURRENT
OI_C = CAPACITOR CURRENT
OI_R = RESULTANT CURRENT
$\cos \phi_1$ = LOAD POWER FACTOR
$\cos \phi_2$ = FINAL POWER FACTOR
OI_W = ENERGY COMPONENT
OI_C = $OI_L \sin \phi_1 - OI_R \sin \phi_2$

Fig. 1.

DIAGRAM FOR CAPACITORS

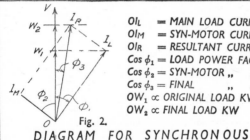

OI_L = MAIN LOAD CURRENT
OI_M = SYN-MOTOR CURRENT
OI_R = RESULTANT CURRENT
$\cos \phi_1$ = LOAD POWER FACTOR
$\cos \phi_2$ = SYN-MOTOR „   „
$\cos \phi_3$ = FINAL   „   „
$OW_1 \propto$ ORIGINAL LOAD KW
$OW_2 \propto$ FINAL LOAD KW

Fig. 2.

DIAGRAM FOR SYNCHRONOUS MOTOR

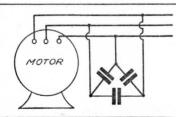

SUPPLY   Fig. 3.

CAPACITORS CONNECTED IN DELTA FOR THREE-PHASE

MOTOR

The Financial Side of Power Factor.—The industrial consumer pays for low power factor in two ways—first, on the initial cost of the installation : second, on the supply charges. Typical two-part tariffs for power users consist of a fixed, or maximum demand, charge of from £8 15s. to £13 per kVA or per kW of maximum demand, and a " unit " charge of from 0·79d. to 1·1d. or more per kWh of energy consumed. Furthermore most of these tariffs are based on a fixed number of kVA or kW's, with a reduced m.d. per kW or per kVA, for higher quantities of power. The unit charge also decreases above a certain number of units consumed.

Taking the case of the 300-kW loads, one at 0·9 and the other at 0·6 power factor, with a tariff of £10 per kVA, plus 0·9d. per kWh, and an annual service of 2,000 hours in each case, the annual bills from the supply company will be :

(1) For the 0·9 power factor load :

	£	s.	d.
333⅓ kVA at £10	3 333	6	8
300 × 2 000 kWh at 0·9d. . .	2 250	0	0
Total.	5 583	6	8

(2) For the 0·6 power factor load :

	£	s.	d.
500 kVA at £10	5 000	0	0
300 × 2 000 kWh at 0·9d. . .	2 250	0	0
Total. . . .	£7 250	0	0

Thus the low-power factor consumer pays over £1 667 per annum on his electricity bill more than his high-power factor neighbour.

How the Bill can be Reduced.—The low-power factor consumer can reduce his bill by installing capacitors to improve his power factor. If the power factor is to be improved to 0·9, a capacitor of about 250 kVA will be required, which will cost between £800 and £1 100 according to the voltage. With this outlay the consumer will save from £500 to £800 during the year the capacitor is installed, and £1 667 during each subsequent year.

These simple methods show how a decision can be arrived at as to whether an improved power factor obtained by the addition of correcting equipment is a financial proposition or not where a maximum demand tariff is in force.

If a bonus and/or penalty system of charges is in force, the calculation of the reduction in power bill is obviously very similar to the above, while the calculation for the cost of improvement of power factor is, of course, the same.

Examples on the use of synchronous motors as capacitors.

(1) Assume a load of 450 kilowatts at 0·65 power factor. It is desired to raise the power factor to 0·9. What will be the rating of the synchronous motor ?

Solution.—We will assume we have to start with 450 kilowatts at 0·65 power factor, or

$$450 \times \frac{1}{0·65} = 690 \text{ kVA}$$

which has a component of $\sqrt{690^2 - 450^2} = 525$ wattless kilovolt-amps. lagging.

With the energy load unchanged and the power factor raised to 0·9, we will have $450 \times \frac{1}{0·9} = 500$ kVA which will have a component of $\sqrt{500^2 - 450^2} = 220$ wattless kilovolt-amps. lagging. It is obvious that the capacitor must supply the difference between the 525 kilovolt-amps, and 220 kilovolt-amps, or 305 wattless kilovolt-amps. leading. A standard 300-kilovolt-amps. synchronous motor would meet this case.

(2) It is desired to add 150 kilowatts load to the 450 kilowatts load at 0·65 power factor, but at the same time raise the power factor of the plant to 0·9. What will be the rating of the synchronous motor to supply this energy load and at the same time raise the power factor of the system from 0·65 to 0·9 ?

Solution.—We will have, as before, 450 kilowatts at 0·65 power factor, or, as we have 600 kilovolt-amps. with a watt-less component of 525 kilovolt-amps., the load will be increased from 450 to (450 + 150) = 600 kilowatts and with the power factor raised to 0·9, we will have an apparent kilovolt-amps. of 670 with a wattless component of $\sqrt{670^2 - 600^2} = 300$ kilovolt-amps. Thus, we must supply in leading kilovolt-amps. the difference between 525 kilovolt-amps. and 300 kilovolt-amps. or 225 kilovolt-amps. The synchronous motor then must supply 150 kilowatts and 225 kilovolt-amps. wattless which would give it a rating of $\sqrt{225^2 + 150^2} = 290$ kilovolt-amps.

The actual input, of course, would be slightly greater than 290 kilovolt-amps.

ELECTRICITY TARIFFS AND COSTS

As electricity is not a commodity which can be stored and used as required, the flat-rate basis was found unsatisfactory and two-part tariffs in some form or another are rapidly replacing fixed-rate tariffs of so much per unit.

The two-part tariff is based on two costs of which the first part is covered by an annual amount and the second part by a charge per unit used.

Load Factor.—This can be defined as the average load compared with the maximum load for any given period. It can be calculated as follows :

$$\frac{\text{Actual energy consumed}}{\text{Maximum demand} \times \text{Time in hours of period}}$$

The load factor of a consumer may vary from as low as 5 per cent. to as high as 80 per cent., but usually it ranges from 10 per cent. (for lighting only) to 40 per cent. (for industrial or heating loads). Some industries are able to offer a 24-hour load and it is in these cases that very high load factor figures are obtained.

Owing to the two-part nature of the cost of supplying electrical energy, the actual load factor has a direct effect on the cost per unit since the fixed or standing charge to cover the first cost is divided into all the units used during that period. The more units used (and the higher the load factor), the less will be the fixed cost per unit. On this account it is the aim of every supply engineer to make his load factor as high as possible. As will be explained, special inducements are generally offered to consumers who will enable him to do this.

Diversity.—The diversity of the supply load is given by the *diversity factor*, which is found from

$$\frac{\text{Sum of consumers' maximum demands}}{\text{Maximum demand on system}},$$

and it will be seen that

$$\frac{\text{System load factor}}{\text{Average consumer's load factor}} = \text{Diversity factor}.$$

Note.—The average consumer's load factor must be calculated with reference to actual consumptions and not merely as a numerical average.

Two-part Tariffs.*—These are usually of three† different types, *industrial, commercial* and *domestic.*

An industrial two-part tariff is always based on the maximum demand—either in kW or in kVA. A typical industrial tariff will therefore be

£8 15s. per annum per kW of maximum demand for the first 20 kW plus 1·1d. per unit consumed for the first 150 units. The maximum demand charge is reduced to £8 10s. for the next 180 kW with a unit charge of 0·72d. for the next 250, and so on.

It is more usual to-day to base the fixed charge on kVA so that the supply authority is compensated for any consumer taking his supply at a low power factor. Another method is to allow for power factor by means of an additional clause, varying the cost per unit by an amount proportional to the power factor *above or below* a datum of, say, 0·85. In this way the consumer is recompensed if he has a high power factor.

The maximum demand figure is obtained by means of a maximum demand indicator which gives the highest load (either in kW or kVA according to the tariff) which occurs for a given period—such as 15 or 30 minutes.

Special tariffs are in many cases offered to consumers with favourable loads. Examples of this are for shop-window lighting after ordinaryhours, night loads of every description including off-peak thermal storage heating, and for 24-hour loads (such as electric processes running continuously) additional concessions are often made over and above the low figures automatically obtained by the two-part tariff. In some cases Electricity Boards have a cheaper summer rate than winter.

Bulk supply tariffs to large consumers also include a clause varying the consumption figure per unit according to the price of coal above or below a certain price per ton.

Fixed simple flat rate charges are still in use for small consumers.

---

* Based on *The Electrical Times Handbook*, 1965, for the London Electricity Board. Other Boards are very similar.
† Most supply authorities have two other tariffs, for Churches, and farms. Domestic tariffs take the form of a quarterly charge plus a charge of about 1·7d. per unit. The Commercial block tariff rate is usually based upon a high unit charge for a limited number of units for lighting, heating, water heating and cooking, private rooms and motors with a reduced unit charge for the excess.

MERCURY-ARC RECTIFIERS

FOR many applications of power conversion the rotary machine has been superseded by the mercury-arc rectifier or the solid state rectifier (see the next section) devices which afford a direct conversion of energy without any intermediary mechanical stage as in rotary plant and which indeed are essentially static, with the consequent advantage of greater simplicity in construction and control, greater reliability and, in all but a few applications, higher efficiency.

The principle of the mercury-arc rectifier was discovered by Cooper Hewitt, who observed the rectifying properties exhibited by his Cooper Hewitt mercury-arc lamps, and his first patent leading to the practical utilization of this property dates back to about 1903. The first mercury-arc rectifiers were consequently of the glass-bulb type, and it is interesting to note that although other types of rectifier have been developed from it, the glass-bulb rectifier is still the most popular form in Great Britain, and is utilized for a surprisingly wide range of applications from battery charging up to supplying electric railway systems.

The first rectifiers were small and used on such minor tasks as battery charging. By 1914 single bulbs carrying 100 amps. and more were in service. After this date more rapid development took place and soon bulbs were produced to carry 500–600 amps. at voltages up to 600 volts. Bulbs operating at higher voltages such as 1 200 and 1 500 volts for traction and special h.v. bulbs operating at 20 to 30 kV are also now in use.

Based on Cooper Hewitt's patents of 1908 and 1911, a simultaneous development of the steel-tank rectifier took place chiefly in America and on the Continent and subsequently, in Great Britain, where this type is now extensively manufactured.

The third type of mercury-vapour rectifier, the hot-cathode pattern, is of mixed origin, combining the electron-emitting properties of a heated filament (familiar in the wireless valve) with the property of mercury vapour to reduce the resistance of the electron path, the mercury vapour being obtained by introducing a small quantity of mercury into the bulb.

Principle of Operation.—In a rectifier the electron stream comprising the arc must be generated by some emitting source which may be the heated filament of the hot-cathode rectifier or, as in the case of the mercury-pool rectifier, the surface of the mercury cathode raised to incandescence by an arc. In practice this incandescence is first generated by drawing an arc from the mercury by means of a movable auxiliary electrode and this "hot spot" is subsequently maintained automatically by the action of the main rectifier arc, as explained later.

The hot spot serves a dual purpose :

(a) To maintain an atmosphere of mercury vapour inside the bulb.

(b) To provide a stream of free electrons.

If a positively charged electrode (anode) is placed near to the hot spot, the electrons from this source are attracted to the positive electrode at high velocity, and in this process collide with the mercury-vapour atoms from which further free electrons are thus liberated. These liberated electrons join the main electron stream which comprises the " mercury arc." The mercury-vapour atoms from which electrons have been liberated are left as (positively charged) ions which neutralize the negative space charge above the cathode (thus greatly reducing the resistance of the electron path) and also by bombardment of the cathode pool, due to mutual attraction, serve to maintain the incandescence of the hot spot.

By far the greatest flow of current will be from the cathode to the anode due to the large volume of the electron stream. A small, and for practical purposes, negligible reverse current also occurs due to the relatively small number of ionized mercury-vapour atoms moving in the opposite direction. This unidirectional phenomenon is responsible for the valve action of the rectifier.

The neutralization of the space charge mentioned reduces the voltage drop in the arc to a constant value per unit length of arc path. For the usual sizes of rectifiers the value of voltage drop in the arc will be of the order of 15–30 volts.

The constant value of this voltage drop is responsible for an important feature of the rectifier as compared with rotating machinery in that the power loss in the rectifier increases directly and not as the square of the load current. This also explains the flatness of the efficiency curve for a rectifier.

133

MERCURY ARC RECTIFIERS

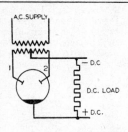

A.C. SUPPLY

1   2

— D.C

D.C. LOAD

+ D.C.

FIG. 1
ESSENTIAL FEATURES
OF SINGLE - PHASE
RECTIFIER

SINGLE — PHASE

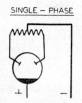

+   —

3 — PHASE

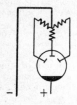

—   +

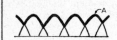

6 — PHASE

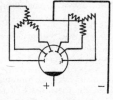

+   —

FIG. 2
THE HEAVY CURVES "A" SHOW OUTPUT WAVE
FORMS NEGLECTING OVERLAP

The basic operation of the mercury-arc rectifier is simply illustrated in Fig. 1.

The a.c. is supplied to the rectifier bulb through a transformer of which the ends of the secondary winding are connected to the anodes (1 and 2) and the centre forms one pole (the negative) of the d.c. output. The ends of the transformer secondary (and therefore the rectifier anodes) reverse their polarity at the frequency of the a.c. supply, and assuming that the electron stream or arc has been initiated by auxiliary means as already mentioned, it will be attracted to the positive anode, and as each anode becomes positive in turn, so the arc will transfer from one to the other, since due to the repulsion effect of a negative anode on the (negative) electron stream and to the fact that the anode is not an electron-emitting source an arc cannot be sustained between the cathode and a negative anode.

It will be obvious, therefore, from the diagram that the electron flow will always be *from* the cathode to the (momentarily) positive end of the transformer winding, the effect of this being that the flow of current in the output circuit is always in the same direction, i.e. is direct current. The conventional direction of current flow is opposite to that of the electron stream, so that the cathode forms the positive terminal for the load.

It will also be seen that an anode allows current to flow for only one half of each cycle (i.e. while it is positive with respect to the cathode).

By using a number of anodes in conjunction with suitable transformer connections, full-wave 2-phase, 3-phase, 6-phase, etc., rectification can be obtained. Fig. 2 shows representative connections and the unsmoothed d.c. wave form obtained with each.

Due to inductance in the circuit (in the transformer windings, etc.), the firing of each anode overlaps its neighbour, reducing the unsmoothed ripple to an r.m.s. value of about 66 per cent of the average d.c. voltage in the case of two-phase rectification, 25 per cent in the case of 3-phase, 6 per cent in the case of 6-phase, and 1 per cent in the case of 12-phase rectification. All these values are very considerably reduced in practice by the inclusion of series smoothing chokes when required.

When employing 6-phase or 12-phase rectification, the rectifier transformer is most commonly connected in double or quadruple star or in fork. Multiple star connection is the simplest arrangement and by the employment of interphase transformers to couple the secondary star points, anode over-lap can be doubled, thereby reducing the instantaneous value of the anode current with a corresponding reduction in heating and better utilization of transformer windings. The inclusion of interphase transformers introduces a steep voltage drop of 15 to 20 per cent from no load to about 1 per cent load, but as a rectifier seldom operates on such a very low load this is rarely of importance. When necessary, this character-istic can be overcome by a modification of the interphase circuit or other means.

A rectifier, like a transformer, gives a constant and fixed output voltage bearing a direct relationship to the supply voltage. Means of controlling the voltage include the pro-vision of a variable resistance for small capacity plant, tappings on the rectifier transformer arranged either for on-load or off-load control, the provision of a separate in-duction regulator, or grid control.

Grid Control.—This entails the insertion of an insulated metal " grid " in the arc path to each anode and its connection to an appropriate terminal. The principles of grid control are dealt with in connection with the hot cathode rectifier (page 26).

Phase and sometimes amplitude systems of grid excitation are suitable, the equipment required being a small induction regulator for phase control, and a small transformer and potentiometer for amplitude control. For precision, peaky voltage or steep-fronted grid impulses are desirable, variation of the rectified voltage being obtained by altering the phase relationship of the impulses with respect to the anode voltage. The generation of potential impulses may be performed by thermionic valves or magnetic saturation circuits.

Construction of Various Types.—The construction of the four types of mercury arc rectifiers, which have tended to develop along different lines, will be briefly described:

A. Hot-Cathode Rectifiers.—Valves are now made in sizes up to 50 to 60 amps., though larger outputs can be obtained by paralleling several valves. The rectifier normally consists of a valve or valves, an air- or oil-cooled transformer which may be either double wound or auto, and a delay device to allow time for the valve filaments to heat up before load is taken. Switches and meters, etc., can be provided as required, and the whole assembly is usually enclosed in a metal case. Due to the short arc path, the efficiency is high and the filaments of modern valves have a life of several thousand hours. It must be noted, however, that their life, while long, is definitely limited by that of the filament, involving replacement of the valve at intervals, a point which should receive due consideration with the purchase price. These rectifiers are widely used for battery charging and for feeding small cinema arcs and other low-power applications.

B. Glass-Bulb Mercury-Pool Rectifiers.—Bulbs are made in sizes from 10 amps. to 500 amps. and there are glass-bulb rectifier substations in service giving up to 60 kA at 500 volts, i.e. 30 MW, obtained by a compact banking (paralleling) of a number of rectifier units. The splitting up of a large substation capacity into a number of smaller parallel units in this manner has definite advantages in giving increased reliability since if one unit fails the remainder will normally continue to function until the faulty unit receives attention.

In small sizes of up to 100 amps. or so, an air-cooled transformer is situated in the same sheet-metal cubicle as the bulb and excitation gear. A fan may be provided to cool the bulb at its higher ratings. In larger sizes, the transformer is oil immersed in a tank standing alongside the bulb cubicles. Each of the bulbs is mounted in a special cradle in a cubicle with anode fuses and reactors, fan motor and excitation gear. Rectifiers of this type are able to withstand heavy overloads, which together with their high efficiency has made them particularly prominent in the traction field supplying trolley buses, electric trains, etc. Typical efficiencies are from 92 per cent at ¼ load to 94 per cent at full load, and standard overloads are given for different services in B.S. 1698 : 1950.

The steel cubicle units in which the glass-bulbs rectifiers are constructed lead to a compact arrangement, easily installed without need of special foundations and comparing favourably in the matter of floor-space even on large installations with their rivals in this latter field, the steel-tank rectifier. Operation of the glass-bulb rectifier is extremely simple. The a.c. circuit-breaker may normally be left closed (although the a.c. supply must be isolated if the cubicle is opened for inspection or maintenance) and putting the rectifier into service involves merely the closing of the d.c. circuit-breaker. When the d.c. circuit-breaker is closed the cathode " hot spot " is automatically initiated by means of the ignition electrode and the arc is then maintained by means of the exciter electrodes, which comprise in effect a

137

very small single-phase rectifier within the main bulb and whose object is to maintain the cathode hot spot and the necessary mercury-vapour atmosphere inside the bulb, even though there is no load on the main anodes. As soon as the load comes on to the rectifier the main anodes come into operation, the arc to these becoming brighter as the load increases. The whole of this operation is entirely automatic.

It is important to note that while the first cost of the glass bulbs used in this type of rectifier may appear relatively high, nothing is consumed in the bulb, the vaporized mercury merely condensing in the upper part of the bulb and flowing back to the cathode, so that the useful life of the bulb is indefinitely long, extending in a great many cases to over 25 years. Statistics of one company show that in over 500 MW of Hewittic rectifiers installed over a period of 15 years, 97 per cent of the original bulbs are still in service, a significant comment on both the long life and robustness of these units.

The latest development, however, is the introduction of the cooled-cathode rectifier, the advantages of which are increased overall efficiency, especially at the lower voltages, and considerable reduction in the amount of floor space required by the equipment.

In the original type of bulb, the mercury forming the cathode pool is contained direct in the glass base of the bulb; the mercury does not " wet " on to the glass and no meniscus is formed. The cathode spot darts about rapidly on the surface of the mercury as a consequence of the reaction forces resulting from the rapid vaporization of the metal.

For many years it has been known that the cathode spot could be fixed by a metal such as molybdenum or tungsten projecting above the mercury surface. The principle is that the metal must be " wetted " by the mercury, so that an upward curving meniscus is formed.

The bulb is made from the same tough glass as the conventional type but the base has been replaced by a metallic plate perfectly sealed to the glass. Therefore the mercury forming the cathode is in direct contact with this plate.

Attached to the base plate is a suitably-conditioned molybdenum ring which protrudes a little above the surface of the mercury to provide for the formation of an upward meniscus. It is to this meniscus that the cathode spot always drifts and becomes anchored, so that instead of darting rapidly about on the surface of the mercury as in the conventional bulb, it develops into a glow discharge which at full load

138

subtends about three-quarters of the periphery. The arc is struck in the normal manner with the standard starting equipment and is maintained by the exciter electrodes at a low voltage.

C. Steel Tank Mercury-Pool Rectifiers.—These are essentially high-capacity rectifiers and are made for outputs of about 200 amps. and upwards to 6 000 amps. or more in a single unit. The smaller sizes from 200 to 1 500 amps. are air cooled and mounted in cubicles in a similar fashion to glass bulbs, while the larger units usually having 12, 18 or 24 anodes are erected on special foundations in a substation, and provided with water cooling. Formerly, due to the slightly porous nature of the steel tank and its insulated seals, it was necessary to have a rotary vacuum pump, automatically controlled by the state of the vacuum inside the rectifier. Later developments produced for the smaller sizes a tank of special steel fitted with non-porous vitreous enamel seals, which is claimed to hold its vacuum indefinitely. The pumped type of rectifier is now practically obsolete.

D. Ignitron Rectifiers.—Sealed ignitrons of the rectifier type are now available and provide a convenient means of power conversion from 40 kW up to those ratings where a multianode tank is generally recommended (500 kW to 1 000 kW depending upon the application). At low d.c. output voltages, for instance, 250 volts, the ignitron rectifier shows some advantages as regards efficiency. The ignitron rectifier is particularly suitable for portable installations.

Performance and Characteristics of Mercury-Arc Rectifiers.—The main source of power loss in a mercury-arc rectifier occurs in the mercury arc itself. The arc resistance varies little, however, and hence the efficiency of a rectifier increases with the output voltage. For this reason also the efficiency is almost constant from very light loads to very heavy overloads.

The inherent voltage regulation depends upon the reactance of the rectifier transformer. A usual minimum value is 5 per cent. to 6 per cent. from light load to full load, though the regulation may be increased to any desired value by the inclusion of reactance in the anode circuits.

The power factor is a function of the number of phases, but it also depends on the anode and transformer reactance and the load current. Average power factors obtained at full load are 0·86 for 2-phase, 0·83 for 3-phase, 0·93 for 6-phase, and 0·95 for 12-phase connections.

The usual tests carried out on mercury-arc rectifiers include the measurement of the no-load losses and the voltage regulation. Efficiency is most accurately assessed by adding the losses of the transformer and rectifier to the output to give the input power.

Interference Suppression.—Consequent on the nature of the process of rectification, a small a.c. component or ripple is always superimposed on the d.c. output. With the usual smoothing chokes employed, this is not sufficiently prominent to interfere with most electrical machinery. Rectifiers are occasionally found to interfere with wireless reception due to local conditions. The interference may be either low frequency, detected by a continuous background hum in a loud speaker, or high frequency, giving a continous crackling or mush which drowns reception on certain wavebands only. L.F. interference is due to the alternating harmonics superimposed on the d.c. voltage and is eliminated at the source by suitably designing the rectifier transformer or by the addition of a tuned filter circuit to the rectifier. H.F. interference is easily disposed of either at the source or at the receiver by earthing each main through a 1 microfarad capacitor.

METAL RECTIFIERS

THE copper-oxide rectifier was first produced on a commercial scale in 1927 and equipments were built ranging from extremes of half a million volts at a low current to 12,000 amperes at a low voltage. The selenium rectifier was developed a few years later and has now replaced the copper-oxide rectifier for power conversion purposes, being smaller, cheaper and more efficient. The copper-oxide rectifier is, however, still widely used for instrument applications and high-frequency circuits.

Two widely used types of selenium rectifier are the " Westalite " selenium-compound type and the " SenTerCel " rectifier. These are available in a wide range of sizes for many hundreds of applications. The notes on the following pages give brief details of these together with typical circuit diagrams.

An interesting development of the " Westalite " selenium-compound rectifier was the introduction of " double-voltage " and " quadruple-voltage " types. The " double-voltage " rectifier operates at about twice the usual voltage, whilst not appreciably affecting the current rating. Bulk and weight are approximately halved, while efficiencies of 87–92 per cent are obtainable in commercial rectifiers of conventional design. The demand for a high-voltage low-current rectifier for cathode-ray tubes has increased enormously with the developments in television. Hitherto valve rectifiers have been used, but the design of a reliable transformer, with the filament winding insulated for working at several thousand volts above earth, is expensive. This has led to the production of a " quadruple-voltage " rectifier in which the reverse resistance has been increased so that less elements are required. Rectifiers of this type for a peak voltage of 2,000 per inch length of unit are now in operation.

Range of Sizes.—The range of practical sizes, with their usual duties, is of interest.

400,000 volts at	10 milliamperes for X-ray work.	
60,000 volts at	0·25 ampere for electrostatic precipitation.	
5,000 volts at	2 amperes for anode supply to transmitting valves.	
600 volts at	10 amperes	
400 volts at	25 amperes	for general d.c. supply.
230 volts at	50 amperes	
100 volts at	100 amperes for battery charging.	
6 volts at	12,000 amperes or more, for electro-deposition.	

The smallest sizes built are used with moving-coil instruments for reading a.c. voltages and currents, the actual rectifier delivering 1 milliampere at about 200 millivolts, while a special rectifier for use in radio receivers at frequencies of 1,500 kilocycles to handle 100 micro-amperes has also been developed. Larger currents at the various voltages may be justified under unusual conditions.

Circuits.—Several circuits have already been devised as being the most economical to employ under various circumstances. The rectifier is shown as an arrow mark in the diagrams, current flowing in the direction of the arrow-head but not in the opposite sense. (When more than one arrow-head is shown, the combination is built as one complete unit.)

Diagrams showing the voltage and current wave-forms, and how they should be measured, are included. Great care must be exercised in selecting the correct type of instrument, i.e. moving-coil or moving-iron, or misleading results will occur.

The economical sizes of the rectifiers employed in the various circuits, and the purposes for which they are supplied, are as follows (see page 143):

Ref. 1.—D.C. selection by change of polarity of supply. Outputs up to 50 watts. Mainly used with telephone type relays in G.P.O. circuits.

Ref. 2. Surge Absorber.—When a solenoid—such as the field system of a large alternator—is energized, there is a negligible leakage of current through the rectifier. When the solenoid is switched out of circuit, the inductive energy allows the current to die down gradually, without any pressure surge, by flowing in the closed circuit formed by the rectifier and solenoid. The flux gradually collapses, so the principle is often used as a time delay action. Relays shunted with rectifiers will hold up for about a second after the power is cut off.

Ref. 3. Half-Wave.—The only application of this circuit is in connection with vibrating screens, employed for sieving coal, stone, etc.

Ref. 4. Half-Wave and Capacity.—The economical output depends on the current rather than the watts required— 50 milliamperes at voltages between 100 and 5,000 being the economical maximum. The system is often applied to radio receivers designed to operate on a.c. or d.c. mains, and for small contactors or relays requiring about 5 watts when energized from 230-volt a.c. mains.

Ref. 5. Series Shunt.—A large inductance is essential to this system—an air-gap in the iron circuit, as in a contactor,

REF.	DESCRIPTION	CIRCUIT DIAGRAM	WAVE FORM VOLTAGE ACROSS LOAD	WAVE FORM CURRENT THROUGH LOAD	CORRECT INSTRUMENTS VOLTAGE	CORRECT INSTRUMENTS CURRENT
1	D.C. SELECTOR				M.C. or M.I.	M.C. or M.I.
2	SURGE ABSORBER				M.C. or M.I.	M.C. or M.I.
3	HALF WAVE				M.C. × 2	M.C. × 2
4	HALF WAVE AND CAPACITY				M.C.	M.C.
5	SERIES SHUNT				M.C.	M.I.
6	CENTRE TAP				M.I.	M.I.
7a	SINGLE PHASE RESISTANCE LOAD				M.I.	M.I.
7b	INDUCTIVE LOAD				M.C.	M.I.
7c	BATTERY LOAD				M.C. or M.I.	M.C.
8	3 PHASE HALF WAVE				M.I.	M.I.
9	3 PHASE FULL WAVE				M.C. or M.I.	M.C. or M.I.

may make the circuit inoperative. Outputs up to 25 watts are economical.

Ref. 6. Centre-tap. This finds wide use in the radio industry. It is employed in conjunction with valve rectifiers where the two anodes and single cathode are accommodated in one envelope, and it is sometimes convenient to retain the same circuit when replacing a valve with a metal rectifier.

Ref. 7. Bridge.—This circuit is used in the majority of instances where d.c. power is required. The voltage and current wave-form under various conditions of loading are shown. The most common types of load characteristic are inductive (see 7b) and battery charging (7c). A filter system is not required when relays, magnet coils, etc., or other small solenoids are energized from a single-phase bridge rectifier as there is generally sufficient inductance to smooth the current wave so as to prevent chatter.

When charging batteries, some form of ballasting is necessary, or the charge rate will be widely influenced by small changes in the supply pressure. A resistance is shown in Fig. 7c ; a choke is used on large chargers, giving higher efficiency and a smoother current wave.

Ref. 8. Three-Phase, Half-Wave.—This circuit has been extensively used in low voltage heavy current rectifiers for electro-deposition power supply.

In the three-phase half-wave circuit, current flows from each phase in turn through one rectifier to the load, returning to the star point of the interconnected-star secondary winding, which is essential to prevent d.c. saturation of the core of the transformer.

Rectifiers of this type are restricted to outputs of 6–8 volts, which is within the rating of a single element, but equipments with up to 6,000 amperes output have been provided.

Ref. 9. Three-Phase, Full-Wave.—This is economical, compared with single-phase full-wave, above 1 kilowatt, but is often used for lower powers when the output is to be smoothed, the reduction in ripple allowing considerable saving in the cost of the filter.

Oil-cooling.—Westalite rectifiers can be operated satisfactorily when immersed in Class B transformer oil, this being of particular value in connection with the power supply to plating and similar electro-chemical processes when heavy currents at low voltages are required, and the atmosphere is often heavily corrosive. It is highly desirable to have the rectifier near the plating baths in order to avoid costly bus-bars.

HOT CATHODE VALVE RECTIFIERS

THE principle of the high vacuum rectifying valve such as is used in radio receivers for supplying d.c. current from a.c. mains is well known.

The valve consists of an electron-emitting cathode surrounded by an anode. The cathode is generally coated with a mixture of barium and strontium oxides and heated by passing a current either through it directly, or through a separate heater which it surrounds but from which it is insulated.

If a positive potential is applied to the anode, electrons are attracted to it and a current passes, the magnitude of which depends upon the anode potential up to a value equal to the total electron discharge of the cathode. This is the saturation current, and a further increase of anode potential will not cause any increase of current.

The total amount of current in this type of valve is relatively small and it has a high impedance owing to the "space charge," viz. the cloud of electrons which surround the anode. The electrons which are farthest from the cathode tend to repel the others back towards the cathode and thus partly neutralize the pull exerted by the positive anode. Fig. 1 (a) shows the characteristic curve of this type of valve.

If a small quantity of an inert gas, such as argon, helium, neon or mercury vapour, be introduced into the valve, quite a low potential, viz. 8 to 15 volts on the anode, is sufficient to ionize the gas, this ionization being due to collision between the gas molecules and the electrons given out by the cathode. The positive ions thus formed travel towards the cathode and neutralize the space charge. A much larger current can therefore pass for a given anode potential. The passage of the current is accompanied by a visible glow, the colour of which depends upon the particular gas used.

The impedance of the valve falls to zero and may even become negative. The voltage drop across the tube being practically constant for all loads, it follows that the current passed by the valve depends only upon the impedance of the circuit ; Fig. 1 (b) shows the typical characteristics of a gas discharge tube. As the mass of the positive ions is very much greater than that of the electrons, their movement is much slower and they contribute but little to the total current, which is almost entirely carried by the electrons.

This sets a limit to the maximum current that can be taken from a gas discharge valve, and it must never exceed the saturation emission of the cathode or bombardment of the emissive surface by positive ions will take place, due to the lack of sufficient electrons to neutralize them.

If the excess of current is great, visible sputtering takes place and sparks are emitted from the cathode. In the case of smaller overloads the sputtering may be invisible, but damage nevertheless ensues and the life of the valve is materially shortened, consequently the peak current must never exceed that specified by the makers.

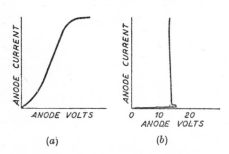

Fig. 1.—Characteristic Curves of a High Vacuum Rectifying Valve and a Gas Discharge Tube.

(a) *High vacuum rectifying valve*; (b) *Gas discharge tube.*

One consequence of this is the necessity of heating the cathode to its operating temperature before the anode circuit is closed. This pre-heating time may, in the case of independently heated and shielded cathodes, be as much as 15 minutes in the mercury discharge type. In the case of the gas discharge tubes it is usually of the order of 30 to 60 seconds. Unfortunately there is no way of avoiding this delay. Time delay switches can be used to make the switching in of the load automatic at the expiration of the required interval.

The gas pressure is very important as a decrease of pressure will reduce the probability of collision and increase the voltage drop across the tube, and bombardment of the cathode will result. There is a critical voltage drop within which the tube must be designed to operate. On the other hand, if the pressure is too high the voltage at which the tube will spark over in the inverse direction is lowered, thus setting a limit on the maximum voltage that can be rectified.

In the case of valves filled with a gas the pressure can vary but little, but where mercury is used, the mercury being in the form of a small globule introduced during evacuation, the pressure will depend on the temperature of the coolest part of the tube, and the maximum inverse voltage that the tube will stand is simply a question of design.

In the case of gas-filled tubes with two or more anodes which are required to give an output of the order of 230/250 volts d.c., the anodes are often placed in separate limbs fused on to the main body of the tube in order to prevent flashover from anode to anode. This type of design sets a limit on the minimum voltage at which the arc will strike. This is of importance only when the load contains a back e.m.f. Such tubes are often constructed with an auxiliary anode which is connected to a small auxiliary rectifier supplying smooth d.c., the current take being of the order of 20 milliamperes. This anode maintains the arc irrespective of the nature of the load.

The absence of resistance in the tube makes rectifiers of high efficiency commercially possible, the usual efficiency of standard equipment being of the order of 85 to 90 per cent at full load and 75 per cent at quarter load, as the only losses in addition to those of the transformer are the wattage used in the heater together with the small drop across the tube which we have seen is independent of load and is of the order of about 6 volts for tubes designed for an anode voltage below 50, and 12 to 16 for those with an anode voltage of 230 and upward. The heater consumption is from 2 to 3 watts per ampere output rating.

The standard commercial equipment caters for two-phase output by means of a centre-tapped secondary winding on the transformer, this tapping providing the negative output, for three-phase by using a three-phase transformer or by direct connection to the mains of the three anodes either in a single tube or in three separate tubes. In the case of six-phase, a three-phase transformer with its secondaries centre tapped is used, the tappings being joined to form the negative.

CONVERTING MACHINES

THE term converting machines is used to cover those arrangements whereby a.c. is converted to d.c. by machines having rotating parts. There are three main types as follows:

Rotary Converters

These consist of a wound rotor revolving in the field of a d.c. generator, the rotor being fitted with slip-rings at one end and with a commutator at the other. If while rotating at synchronous speed an a.c. supply is connected to the slip-rings, d.c. can be taken from the commutator. There is only one winding and the power to keep the machine running and to supply the electrical and friction losses is taken from the a.c. side.

A rotary converter will run from the d.c. side when a.c. can be taken from the slip-rings—this arrangement being called an *inverted rotary converter*. Practically all rotary converters of any size are polyphase—three-phase for small and medium outputs and six-phase for larger outputs.

Ratio of Transformation.—The d.c. voltage will be $\sqrt{2}$ or 1·41 times the a.c. voltage for a single-phase, and the various ratios for polyphase machines are given in the following table:

	Single Phase.	Three Phase.	Six Phase.	Twelve Phase.
Volts between slip-rings as a percentage of d.c. volts . . .	70·7	61·2	35·4	18·3

The relationship is given by a.c. volts between slip-rings $= \dfrac{\text{d.c. volts}}{\sqrt{2}} \sin \dfrac{\pi}{m}$ where $m =$ no. of slip-rings.

As d.c. voltages are usually in the region of 220 to 240 volts it will be seen that with normal a.c. supply a transformer is required to give the required voltage for the supply to the a.c. side.

Six-phase machines are the most usual since it is fairly

A69). The first two of these relate to main switchgear. The main provisions are that every consumer's installation shall be controlled by adequate main switchgear incorporating

(1) means of interrupting the supply in the event of excess current ;
(2) means of interrupting the supply in the event of dangerous earth-leakage ;
(3) means of isolation.

The Regulation also states that if the supply undertaking supplies the main switchgear which can be operated by the consumer, this need not be duplicated by the consumer. Succeeding Regulations deal respectively with isolation of all conductors ; excess-current protection ; overall require-ments for switches ; control and protective devices ; divers-ity ; sub-circuits ; domestic and non-domestic radial and ring circuits ; connection of portable appliances ; and the control of appliances, lighting fittings and motors.

The means of isolation has to be a linked switch suitable for operation on load, or a linked circuit-breaker, arranged to disconnect all circuit conductors of each installation from the supply. For certain 3- and 4-wire systems where one conductor is connected to earth, only the live conductors need to be disconnected by the isolating device, with an isolating link being inserted in the earthed conductor.

Excess-current protection may be by fuses in the live con-ductors or a circuit-breaker fitted with protective trips in the live conductors, although there are certain exceptions. Such protection must be suitable for the maximum short-circuit current attainable.

Regulation A.8 specifies that in a 2-wire installation con-nected to a source of supply having one pole earthed all fuses and single-pole devices must be connected in the live con-ductor only. Double-pole linked devices may however be employed. The succeeding Regulation says that on a non-earthed two-wire installation all switches, circuit-breakers and fuses must be of the double-pole type.

Except as provided in Regulations A.11–13, the next Regulation A.10 states that every conductor in the installation shall be protected against excess current by a fuse or circuit-breaker. The fuse rating must not exceed that of the lowest rated conductor in the circuit being protected, account being taken of the class of excess-current protection afforded by the fuse, i.e. whether it is coarse or close. A circuit-breaker must operate when the circuit protected is subjected to a sustained excess current of 1·5 times the rating of the lowest-rated conductor in the circuit. There are a number of exceptions, notably motor circuits, ring-circuits and spurs.

Where apparatus is to be operated at medium voltage, or where this exists between adjacent low-voltage circuits, all terminals or other fixed live parts not permanently shrouded in insulating material have to be accessible only to authorised personnel or to be enclosed in earthed metal or incombustible insulating material according to Regulation A.16.

An important rule relating to socket-outlets is contained in Regulation A.20 which specifies that in any one room they must all be connected to the same phase, or pole of a 3-wire system. There is an exemption to this rule for non-domestic premises if it is clearly impracticable to do so this.

Regulations A.21–22 deal with diversity. The first states that this must not be allowed for when calculating the conductor size and switchgear for final sub-circuits except for those for cooking appliances as permitted by A.27–29. According to the next Regulation, diversity is permissible in calculating cable and switchgear sizes of circuits other than final sub-circuits provided this is justified.

The number of points which may be supplied from a final sub-circuit of rating not exceeding 15 amperes is limited by their aggregate demand as determined from Table I ; there shall be no other allowance for diversity in the final sub-

TABLE I

ASSUMED CURRENT DEMANDS OF POINTS

Point or Appliance.	Current Demand to be assumed
(a) 15-ampere socket-outlet.	15 amperes.
(b) 13-ampere socket-outlet.	13 amperes.
(c) 5-ampere socket-outlet.	5 amperes.
(d) 2-ampere socket-outlet.	At least $\frac{1}{2}$ ampere.
(e) Lighting outlet.	Current equivalent to the connected load, with minimum of 100 watts.
(f) Electric clock.	May be neglected.
(g) Other fixed or free-standing appliance.	British Standard rated current, or normal current.

circuit and the current rating of the cable must not be exceeded.

A final sub-circuit having a rating exceeding 15 amperes shall not supply more than one point, except as specifically admitted in Regulations A.27–55. For the purpose of this Regulation a cooker-control unit incorporating a socket-outlet is regarded as one point.

In domestic installations, either radial or ring final sub-circuits conforming with Table II may be installed to serve socket-outlets complying to B.S. 1363 or B.S. 2814 and stationary appliances of ratings not exceeding 13 amperes, provided that the general requirements of certain regulations are met. In addition, ring final sub-circuits may serve spurs in accordance with Regulations A.38–40.

Ring-circuits : Special Requirements.—Each circuit conductor of a ring domestic final sub-circuit shall be run in a ring commencing from the distribution board, looping into the terminals of socket-outlets and joint boxes before returning to the same way of the distribution board (A.35).

Similar conditions apply to the earth-continuity conductor except where the ring final sub-circuit is run throughout in metallic conduit, ducts or trunking (A.36).

The conductors forming the final ring sub-circuit shall either be unbroken where they pass through socket-outlets or joint-boxes, or if cut the electrical continuity of the ring circuit must be ensured by suitable joints (A.37).

For ring final sub-circuits to Regulations A.30–33, the total number of spurs must not exceed the total number of socket-outlets and stationary appliances connected in the ring (A.38). For such ring sub-circuits, fused spurs must be connected through fused spur-boxes. The fuse rating must not exceed either that of the cable feeding the spur or 13 amperes. Total current demand of points fed from a spur must not exceed 13 amperes (A.39).

Non-fused spurs in such sub-circuits must be connected to the ring at socket-outlet terminals, joint boxes or at the origin of the ring at the distribution board. Current rating of such spurs must not be less than the ring conductors, and each cannot feed more than two socket-outlets, or one twin socket-outlet, or one stationary appliance.

Cooker Final Sub-circuit.—Cable rating is assessed as follows : 10 amperes plus 30% of total rated current less 10 amperes, plus 5 amperes if a socket-outlet is incorporated in the control unit (A.27).

TABLE II

RADIAL AND RING FINAL SUB-CIRCUITS
(See Regulations A.30–42)

Description and special conditions, if any	Minimum size of cable used throughout		Maximum permissible number of socket-outlets to B.S. 1363 or B.S. 2814 and fixed appliances*	Rating of fuse or circuit-breaker (amperes)
	Rubber- or p.v.c.-insulated	Mineral-insulated		
(a) Radial circuit serving one room only of less than 300 ft.² floor area which is not a kitchen.	0·0045 in.² (7/·029)	0·003 in.²	6, provided that no fixed water-heating appliance shall be connected to any of these points	20
(b) Radial circuit serving rooms other than in (a) above	0·0045 in.² (7/·029)	0·003 in.²	2	20
	0·007 in.² (7/·036)	0·0045 in.²	6	30
(c) Ring circuit, with spurs, if any	0·0045 in.² (7/·029)	0·003 in.²	See Regulations A.38–42	30

* Of rating not exceeding 13 A ; appliances of 15 VA or less may be ignored.

(From I.E.E. Regulations, 14th Edition

156

Purpose of final circuit	(i)	(ii)	(iii)
… than two motors.	motor. + 50% f.l. of remaining motors.	+ 50% f.l. of remaining motors.	+ 80% f.l. of 2nd largest motor. + 60% f.l. of remaining motors.
5. Water-heaters (instantaneous type*).	100% f.l. of largest appliance. + 100% f.l. of second largest appliance. + 25% f.l. of remaining appliances.	—	To be assessed by competent authority.
6. Water-heaters thermostatically controlled. 7. Floor warming installations. 8. Thermal storage space heating installations.	No diversity allowable.		
9. Socket-outlets and fixed appliances in accordance with Table II on page 156.	100% largest fuse- or circuit-breaker rating of individual circuits. + 40% sum of fuse- or circuit-breaker ratings of other circuits.	100% largest fuse- or circuit-breaker rating of individual circuits. + 50% sum of fuse- or circuit-breaker ratings of other circuits.	100% largest fuse- or circuit-breaker rating of individual circuits. + 50% sum of fuse- or circuit-breaker ratings of other circuits.
10. Socket-outlets and fixed appliances other than those listed above.	100% f.l. of largest outlet. + 40% f.l. of other outlets.	100% f.l. of largest outlet. + 75% f.l. of outlets in main rooms (dining-rooms, etc.) + 40% f.l. of remaining outlets.	100% f.l. of largest outlet. + 75% f.l. of other outlets.

* For the purpose of this Table an instantaneous water-heater is deemed to be a water-heater of any loading which heats water only while the tap is turned on and therefore uses electricity intermittently.

operating at a voltage exceeding extra low-voltage must be effectively prevented, by one of the methods below, from giving rise to danger from earth-leakage currents.

(1) Enclosure in an all-insulated form of housing.
(2) Double insulation for an appliance or lighting fitting.
(3) Earthing of exposed metal parts.
(4) Isolation of metal such that it is not liable to come into contact with live parts or with earthed metal.

Exemption is allowed for apparatus and conductors operating at a d.c. voltage not exceeding 110 V under certain conditions of supply.

The next seven Regulations deal with general provisions for earthing, while D.9 states that where isolation of metal is adopted (see 4 above), it must be confined to short isolated lengths of metal used for protection of non-sheathed cables, other than overhead spans of conduit between buildings, or conduit used for protection of h.v. cables in discharge-lighting installations.

Bonding forms the subject of Regulations D.10–15. For bathrooms or showers, suitable protective shrouding must be used for lampholders likely to be touched by the occupant. Switches or other means of control must be inaccessible to a person using the bath or shower. Neither is a stationary appliance having exposed heating elements allowed within touch. To enforce this, there is a ban on socket-outlets except for shaver supply units.

Succeeding Regulations cover protection by fuses, excess-current circuit-breakers and earth-leakage circuit-breakers. Earth-continuity conductors, earthing leads and methods of connection of the latter conclude this section.

Section E. Testing and Inspection

This section, in contrast to the 13th Edition, now only contains the basic requirements to be satisfied in respect of the testing and inspection of installations. The tests for insulation resistance are contained in Regulations E.6–9 and these are summarized on page 379. Earthing and earth testing have been taken out of this section of the Regulations and are now included in Appendix 6. The provisions for these tests are summarized on pages 369 and 370.

Tests ought to be carried out in the following order :

(1) Verification of polarity.
(2) Tests of effectiveness of earthing.

(3) Insulation resistance tests.
(4) Tests of ring-circuit continuity.

It should be noted according to E.1 that these tests should be carried out not only on every new installation but also on every major alteration to an existing installation.

Impedance of each earth-continuity conductor must not exceed 1·0 ohm or not more than 0·5 ohm (see page 369). The earth-loop impedance at the consumers' terminals is related to the current-rating of the protective device and Regulation D.22 and Table D.1 gives these values for excess-current circuit-breakers, fuses and semi-enclosed fuses. The insulation resistance value must not be less than 1 megohm (see page 379).

Regulation E.14 states that the following notice of durable material must be fixed in a prominent position at or near the main distribution board of every installation upon completion of work. It must be inscribed in print not smaller than 12-point.

" IMPORTANT

This installation should be periodically inspected and tested, and a report on its condition obtained, as prescribed in the Regulations for the Electrical Equipment of Buildings issued by The Institution of Electrical Engineers."

Completion and inspection certificates are to be made out and the form that these should take are indicated at the end of the section.

Section F. Materials and Construction of Apparatus

This section opens with a list of the appropriate British Standards to which the materials, appliances, accessories, fittings and other apparatus should apply and the relevant Regulation. Lamps and lighting fittings are the subject of F.3, while plugs and socket-outlets are covered by the next six Regulations. Extra-low-voltage circuits and special low-voltage circuits are exempt from some of these Regulations. Thus, F.7 exempts the connections for electric clocks provided they are designed for that purpose and the plug incorporates a fuse not exceeding 3 A rating. Shaver connections are also exempt under specified conditions. Cable couplers and connectors, socket-outlet adaptors, resistors and machine-control gear are the subjects of F.10-12.

Section G. Electric Discharge Lighting Circuits

There are two divisions in this section, the first six Regulations applying to all electric discharge-lighting installations, while the remaining 20 are for systems where the voltage exceeds 650 V r.m.s. when measured on open-circuit.

Unless specially designed for inductive circuits, the switch must have a current rating of not less than twice the total steady load current which it is required to carry. If used to control filament lighting and discharge lighting, the current rating must not be less than the sum of the filament lamp current and twice the total steady current of the discharge lamp (G.2).

Current-carrying capacity of discharge circuits must take account of total steady current, the gear and also its harmonics (G.3).

Transformers and inductors must be installed as near as is practicable to the associated discharge lamp (G.4).

Live parts must be effectively screened, motor-generators and motor-convertors must be permanently earthed at a terminal, and 5 kV is the maximum voltage permissible (G.5–7).

Other Regulations are concerned with h.v. ancillary equipment, h.v. transformers exceeding 500 W rating, separation of h.v. circuits from the mains supply, isolation of circuits supplying h.v. lamps and fireman's switch. Cables, clearances and creepages and earthed return conductors as used for discharge lighting are referred to in Regulations G.15–26.

Section H. Temporary Installations

Besides having to comply with the requirements of the Regulations for permanent installations, temporary installations have two further Regulations to which they must conform, namely H.2 and 3. The detailed requirements for cable supports outlined in B.33 relating to permanent installations need not be observed provided the support system adopted places no appreciable strain on the cable terminations and joints.

Attention is drawn to Regulations dealing with polarity, switch connections, mechanical damage, dampness and corrosion. Where possible, supply should be at 110 V by means of a double-wound transformer, or if this is not practicable the adoption of monitored earthing circuits or other devices is suggested. For two-wire supplies, double-pole switches and/or linked circuit-breakers must be employed.

	Recommended Illumination lm/ft^2	Limiting Glare Index
PLASTICS WORKS		
Moulding—compression, injection ; sheet fabrication—shaping, cementing	20	25
Sheet fabrication—trimming, machining, polishing	30	25
PRINTING WORKS		
Type foundries	20	25
Printing plants:		
machine composition, imposing stones	20	25
composing rooms	45	19
proof reading	30	19
Photo-engraving :		
block-making etching, masking	20	25
finishing and routing	30	25
TEXTILE MILLS, COTTON OR LINEN		
Bale breaking, blowing, carding, roving, slubbing, etc.	15	25
Warping, slashing, dressing and dyeing, doubling, spinning	20	25
Healding	70	—
Weaving : patterned cloths, fine counts dark	30	19
plain " grey " cloth	20	19
Cloth inspection	70*	19
TEXTILE MILLS, SILK OR SYNTHETIC		
Soaking, fugitive tinting, conditioning or setting of twist	20	25
Spinning	45	25
Winding, twisting, rewinding and coning, quilling and slashing : light thread	20	25
dark thread	30	25
Warping	30	25
Healding, weaving	70	19
Inspection	100*	19
TEXTILE MILLS, WOOLLEN		
Scouring, carbonizing, teasing, preparing, raising, brushing, pressing, backwashing, gilling, crabbing and blowing	15	25
Blending, carding, combing (white), tentering, drying, cropping	20	25
Spinning, roving, winding, warping, combing (coloured), twisting	45	25
Weaving : fine worsteds	70	19
heavy woollens	30	19
Perching : " grey "	370	—
final	200*	—
WAREHOUSES AND BULK STORES		
Large material, loading bays	10	28
Small material, racks	15	25
Packing and despatch	15	25
WOODWORKING SHOPS		
Rough sawing and bench work	15	22
Sizing, planing, rough sanding, medium machine and bench work, glueing, veneering, cooperage	20	22
Fine bench work, fine sanding and finishing	30	22

* Special attention should be paid to the colour quality of the light.

of fittings required may be less. Knowing the spacing in each direction, the number of fittings to be used is known.

3. Choose a suitable type of fitting for the interior, bearing in mind the work done there and the people doing it. The way in which the light is required to be distributed from the fitting is the most important factor (Fig. 1).

4. Having chosen the type of fitting, estimate the losses of light which occur from the time it leaves the lamps to the time it reaches the working plane. This will depend on a number of factors—the proportions of the room, the type and efficiency of the fittings, the reflecting power of the ceiling and walls, the mounting height of the lamps—and is found in two steps, (a) by selecting the appropriate Room Index (Table III), and then (b) using this in Table IV to find the Coefficient of Utilization. This latter is the proportion of original lamp light which eventually reaches the working plane—in other words, the luminous efficiency of the installation as a whole.

5. Make a further allowance for the fact that the installation cannot keep its original efficiency owing to deterioration in service of the reflecting and transmitting properties of the fittings due to natural soiling, and to some deterioration in the decorations. Lacking further guidance, it is assumed that the average performance in service will, due to these causes, be 80 per cent. as high as initially. Normally, then, the *Maintenance Factor* is 0·8. This assumes a reasonable cleaning schedule, without which the efficiency of the installation can, in dusty or dirty locations, fall by as much as 50 per cent. in a few weeks.

6. The lumen output required of each lamp can then be worked out from the formula :

Lumens per lamp

$$= \frac{\text{Illumination required (lm./ft.}^2) \times \text{Total floor area}}{\text{Number of fittings} \times \text{Coefficient of Utilization}} \times \text{Maintenance Factor}$$

and it is then only necessary to refer to Tables V, VI or IX to find a lamp of the required type which has an average light output through life close to the figure indicated by the answer to the formula. If the required lumen output falls half-way between two lamp sizes, choose the larger rather than the smaller, or recalculate with a slightly smaller spacing between fittings than before.

In this process of lighting design, provided that reasonable care is taken, there are only two places where the designer

178

TABLE III.—Room Index

		For Direct and General Fittings.				
	Height of Fitting above Working Plane.	— — —	9' to 10' 6"	11' to 13' 6"	14' to 17'	18' to 21'
		For Semi-Indirect and Indirect Fittings.				
	Height of Ceiling above Floor.	11' to 13' 6"	14' to 17'	18' to 21'	22' to 27'	28' to 33'
Room Width.	Room Length.	Room Index.				
12' (11' 6"– 12' 6")	11½–14 14–20 20–30	B *B* C	*A* *A* B	*A* *A* A	— — —	— — —
17' (16'–18')	16–20 20–30 30–42 42–60	C D D E	B C C D	A B C D/C	A A B/A B	— — A A
24' (23'–26')	23–30 30–42 42–60 60–90	E E F F	D D E E	C D/C D E/D	B B C C	A A B B
28' (27'–30')	27–42 42–60 60–90 90–140	F G G G	E F/E F F	D E E F	C D/C D E	B C C D
33' (31'–36')	31–42 42–60 60–90 90–140	F G H/G H	E F F G	E/D E F F	C D E E	B C D/C D
40' (37'–44')	37–60 60–90 90–140	E F G	D E F	C D E	B C D	B B C/B

NOTE.—Where the indices are given in italic it is preferable to use the point-by-point method of design.

179

TABLE IV.—COEFFICIENTS OF UTILIZATION

System.	Ceiling R.F.	50%			70%		
	Walls R.F.	10%	30%	50%	10%	30%	50%
	Room Index	Coefficient of Utilization.					
Mainly Direct. At least 70% of total light output to lower hemisphere.	A	0·24	0·28	0·32	0·24	0·28	0·33
	B	0·33	0·36	0·40	0·33	0·36	0·41
	C	0·37	0·40	0·43	0·38	0·40	0·44
	D	0·41	0·43	0·46	0·42	0·44	0·47
	E	0·44	0·46	0·49	0·45	0·47	0·50
	F	0·47	0·49	0·52	0·48	0·50	0·53
	G	0·50	0·53	0·55	0·51	0·53	0·56
	H	0·53	0·56	0·58	0·54	0·56	0·59
General. Approximately the same light output upward and downward.	A	0·20	0·23	0·26	0·22	0·25	0·28
	B	0·27	0·29	0·31	0·27	0·30	0·34
	C	0·32	0·34	0·36	0·32	0·34	0·39
	D	0·36	0·38	0·40	0·36	0·38	0·43
	E	0·40	0·42	0·44	0·40	0·42	0·47
	F	0·43	0·45	0·47	0·43	0·45	0·50
	G	0·46	0·48	0·50	0·46	0·48	0·53
	H	0·49	0·51	0·53	0·49	0·51	0·55
Mainly Indirect. At least 75% of total light output to upper hemisphere.	A	—	0·08	0·10	0·10	0·12	0·15
	B	—	0·10	0·12	0·13	0·16	0·18
	C	—	0·12	0·14	0·16	0·19	0·21
	D	—	0·14	0·16	0·19	0·22	0·24
	E	—	0·16	0·18	0·22	0·25	0·27
	F	—	0·18	0·20	0·25	0·28	0·30
	G	—	0·20	0·22	0·27	0·30	0·33
	H	—	0·21	0·23	0·29	0·32	0·36

can go wrong. One is in the choice of type of fitting (and associated type of lamp) and it must be emphasized that the most suitable type for the particular job should always be preferred to a less suitable type which, even though cheaper in first cost, will for several years handicap those who are trying to use it ; the second is that when considering which lamp type to use it is very easy to be over-influenced by a comparison of capital costs. A new installation can be

Type and Wattage	Bulb Shape	Dimensions		Approx. Loss in Choke (Watts).	Average Lumens through Life.	Cap.
		Length mm.	Diameter mm.			
Mercury:						
MB/U 80	Pear	160	80	10	2,700	3-pin B.C.
" 125	Pear	178	90	12	4,900	3-pin B.C.
" 1,000	Tubular	372	65	50	52,000	G.E.S.
MA/V 250	Tubular	290	48	17	8,750	G.E.S.
MA/H 400	Tubular	330	48	25	16,000	G.E.S.
400	Tubular	330	48	25	13,200†	G.E.S.
Fluorescent Mercury:						
MBF/U 80	Pear	160	80	10	2,720	3-pin B.C.
" 125	Pear	178	90	12	4,900	3-pin B.C.
MAF/V 400	Isothermal	335	165	25	12,800	G.E.S.
Tungsten/Mercury:						
MBT/U 160	Pear	178	90	—	2,080	E.S.
" 200	Pear	178	90	—	2,800	E.S.
" 250	Pear	233	110	—	3,500	G.E.S.
MAT/V 300	Tubular	285	85	—	5,400	G.E.S.
" 500	Tubular	355	100	—	10,500	G.E.S.
Mercury, black bulb:						
MBW/U 125	Pear	178	90	12	—	3-pin B.C.
Sodium:						
SO/H 45	Tubular	238	50	23	2,565	B.C.
" 60	Tubular	300	50	23	3,720	B.C.
" 85	Tubular	415	50	23	5,950	B.C.
" 140	Tubular	518	65	30	9,800	B.C.

* This does not list all the various wattages available. † For MA/U in vertical position add 10 per cent.

gear being required. The life of these lamps has recently been increased to 3,000 hours.

No attempt should ever be made to keep an MB or MBF lamp in operation if the outer bulb becomes accidentally broken, for in these types the inner discharge tube of quartz does not absorb potentially dangerous radiations which are normally blocked by the outer glass bulb.

Sodium Lamps.—Sodium lamps give light which is virtually monochromatic ; that is, they emit yellow light at one wavelength only, all other colours of light being absent. Thus white and yellow objects look yellow, and other colours appear in varying shades of grey to black.

However, sodium lamps have a very high efficiency and are widely used for streets where the primary aim is to provide light for visibility at least cost to the rates ; also for floodlighting where a yellow light is acceptable or preferred.

The discharge U-tube is contained within a renewable double-walled vacuum glass jacket which conserves the heat and enables the metallic sodium in the tube to become sufficiently vaporized. Should a sodium lamp not reach full brightness, and continue to give a reddish glow (as at starting), it is probable that the jacket has lost its vacuum and is permitting too much heat to escape. The remedy, of course, is a new jacket.

A leakage transformer is used to provide the relatively high voltage required for starting, and the lower voltage required as the lamp runs up to full brightness—a process taking up to about 15 minutes. A power-factor correction capacitor should be used on the mains side of the transformer primary. Since the three smaller sizes of lamp all take the same current, one transformer can be used for all three sizes.

Sodium lamps are designed to be used horizontally with one limb of the U-tube above the other. They should never be used with the cap lower than the rest of the lamp, as hot sodium may then attack the most vulnerable glass parts near each electrode ; for the same reason they should not be moved when hot. If desired, the two smaller sizes may be used vertically, cap up. Metallic sodium may burn if brought into contact with moisture, therefore care is necessary when disposing of discarded sodium lamps ; a sound plan is to break the lamps in a bucket in the open and pour water on them, then after a short while the residue can be disposed of in the ordinary way. The normal life of all sodium lamps has recently been increased to 4 000 hours with an objective average of 6 000 hours.

FLUORESCENT TUBE LIGHTING

THE fluorescent tubes used in this country consist essentially of a length of tubing coated inside with fluorescent powder and having heater filaments (which also act as electrodes) fused into the end of the tube. The interior of the tube is filled with mercury vapour and argon at low pressure. The elements of a fluorescent tube circuit are shown in Figs. 2 and 3.

Glow Starter Circuit.—As soon as the main circuit switch is closed, the full mains voltage is applied across the electrodes of the glow starting switch. The voltage is sufficient to cause a glow discharge in the starting switch bulb. This has the effect of warming up the bi-metallic strips on which the switch contacts are mounted. The heating of these bi-metallic strips causes them to bend towards each other until the contacts touch. The glow discharge in the starter switch then disappears. The heater elements which form the electrodes in the fluorescent tube are heated by the current which now passes through them. In the meantime the bi-metallic strips not being heated by the glow discharge cool down and spring away from each other. This sudden interruption of the circuit, which contains a choke, causes a voltage surge across the fluorescent lamp electrodes which starts the discharge in the fluorescent lamp.

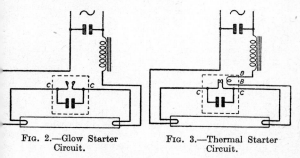

FIG. 2.—Glow Starter
Circuit.

FIG. 3.—Thermal Starter
Circuit.

Thermal Starter Circuit.—In this case it will be seen that the starter switch contains two contacts mounted on bi-metallic strips, the contacts being closed when the lamp is not switched on. The starter switch also contains a small heater coil connected in series with one of the main lamp electrodes.

When the circuit switch is closed, current passes through the choke, the thermal switch heater, the main lamp electrode heaters and the bi-metallic switch contacts. After a short interval the heating of the bi-metallic strips causes them to spring apart. This sudden interruption of the circuit causes a voltage surge across the electrodes of the fluorescent tube. This starts the discharge.

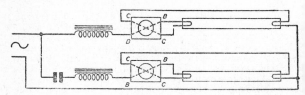

Fig. 4.—Twin-lamp Circuit for 3-ft., 4-ft., and 5-ft. Lamps.

The Twin-Lamp Circuit.—Single fluorescent tubes may suffer from the disadvantage of flicker due to the fact that in an alternating current circuit there is a partial extinction of the light every half cycle. The arrangement illustrated in Fig. 4 enables two lamps to be used in such a way that the instant of partial extinction in one lamp coincides with the instant of near maximum brightness in the other lamp. Thus the two lamps, providing they are arranged reasonably close together, will give almost flickerless lighting.

The Series Circuit.—Fluorescent lamps more than 2 ft. long require one set of control gear each ; lamps of 2 ft. length and less can either be run singly on 100–130 volts or on 200–260 volts (except 40-watt 2-ft.) or, as is generally the case, two in series with a single choke on 200–260 volts. The circuit is shown in Fig. 5 and it will be seen that the lamps will start one after the other. Both must be of the same wattage but not necessarily of the same colour. Thermal type switches are normally used in this circuit because they will prevent the lamps from starting until the electrodes

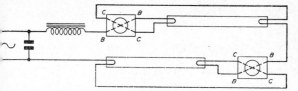

FIG. 5.—Series Operation of Short Fluorescent Lamps with
Switched Starting.

have become hot, but special starters are also available which
will each start a pair of lamps. Series running is economical
since only one choke is necessary per pair of lamps, and
choke losses are small, but if one lamp or starter misbehaves
it may also affect the other lamp; therefore trouble in this
circuit should be investigated as soon as possible. If series-
operated lamps are to be run on a quickstart circuit a double-
wound transformer is needed as shown in Fig. 6, and both
lamps must have the earthed metallic strip.

Instant Starting Circuit.—A fluorescent tube circuit
designed to give a rapid start without flickering is shown
in Fig. 7. The unit consists of an auto-transformer, the
primary winding of which is connected across the fluorescent
tube, with the secondary winding in two separate sections,
one across each cathode.

When the lamp is switched on, practically the whole mains
voltage is applied across the transformer primary and the
cathodes are heated by current from the secondary windings.

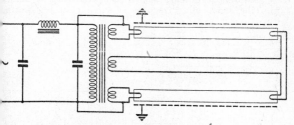

FIG. 6.—Series Operation of Short Fluorescent Lamps with
Quickstart Circuit.

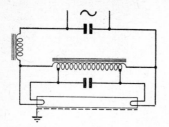

FIG. 7.—Instant-start
Circuit for Single-
lamp Operation.

As soon as the cathodes are hot (this usually takes place in a
fraction of a second) the tube strikes and the voltage across
the primary of the transformer falls to the lamp voltage,
about 110 volts, and the cathode voltages are correspondingly
reduced.

For satisfactory starting it is essential to use lamps with
an external metal strip cemented along the outside (type
MCFA/U) and this strip must be earthed, or alternatively
in some cases the fitting contains earthed metal performing
the same function.

Filament-Ballast Circuits.—There are two standard
methods by which filament lamps can be used to control the
current in fluorescent lamp circuits. In both the filament-
ballast lamp takes the place of the normal choke and power-
factor capacitor, and adds its luminous output to that of the
fluorescent lamp. All circuit components are very light and
the power factor is practically unity. Since the ballast lamps
are of special rating they are fitted with 3-pin caps to prevent
their insertion in ordinary B.C. holders connected to mains.

(a) This arrangement requires a small electrode-heating

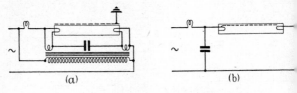

FIG. 8.—Filament-Ballast Circuits.
(a) With lamp and electrode-heating transformer.
(b) With fluorescent lamp.

190

ransformer and a standard instant-start 40-watt (4-ft.) lamp. The ballast lamp is similar in appearance to an ordinary 60-watt pearl lamp.

(b) In this arrangement a special 40-watt (4-ft.) fluorescent amp having an internal starting strip and single contact caps s connected in series with a ballast lamp.

The luminous efficiency of the ballast lamp in each case is bout 11 lm./watt, and the power consumed by it is of the rder of 70 watts, depending on the voltage of the mains. The luminous efficiency of the whole system varies slightly vith mains voltage and colour of fluorescent lamp, but is f the order of 20 lm./watt, i.e. about twice that of small ilament lamps alone, and about half that of fluorescent lamps lone. These circuits are not suitable for use on d.c. supplies.

D.C. Working.—If desired, fluorescent lamps may be used n d.c. supplies by omitting the normal power-factor capaci-or and inserting a suitable resistor in series with the choke. 'his resistor consumes a wattage generally roughly equal to hat of the lamp, so that the luminous efficiency of the circuit s about half of that on a.c. Suitable resistance values are s follows :

TABLE VII

RESISTORS FOR D.C. OPERATION

Mains Voltage.	Resistor Values (Ohms).					
	1–80 W.	1–40 W. (4 ft.)	1–30 W.	2–40 W. (2 ft.)	2–20 W.	2–15 W.
200	103	208	264	116	182	235
210	116	235	293	128	208	264
220	128	264	330	147	235	293
230	147	293	380	147	264	330
240	166	330	420	166	293	380
250	166	330	420	166	330	380

A choke of 240/250 volts rating is recommended for any of the above mains oltages.

After a period of working the positive end of the tube may arken owing to migration of the mercury to the negative nd, and to counteract this tendency it is usual to fit a

TABLE VIII

Tubular Fluorescent Lamps (Type MCF/U)

Lamp Consumption (Watts).	Nominal Lamp Voltage.	Approx. Total Circuit (Watts).	Nominal Lamp Current (Amps).	Overall Length (ft).	Diameter (ins).	Caps Each End.
15	56	7/12*	0·3	1½	1	Bi-pin
20	61	7/12*	0·35	2†	1½	Bi-pin
30	104	12	0·35	3†	1	Bi-pin
40	50	8/15*	0·88	2†	1½	Bi-pin
40	108	10	0·41	4†	1	Bi-pin
50	160	12	0·41	5	1½	Bi-pin
80	106	15	0·85	5	1½	B.C. or Bi-pin
125	170	15	0·90	8	1½	B.C., Bi-pin or R.D.C.

* First two lamps in series of 200/250 v.
† Including standard bi-pin holders.

TABLE IX.—Tubular Fluorescent Lamps—
Average Lumen Output

Rating (Watts).	White.	Warm White.	Day-light.	Natural.	Warm Tone.	Colour Matching.
20	1 050	1 050	960	710	780	700
30	1 740	1 750	1 650	1 300	1 350	1 200
40 (2 ft)	1 500	1 700	1 420	1 080	1 080	1 010
40 (4 ft)	2 580	2 700	2 450	1 900	1 950	1 700
50	—	3 100	—	2 100	—	—
65 \ 65/80	4 300	4 425	4 150	2 950	3 050	2 850
80 /	4 800	4 875	4 600	3 520	3 400	3 150
80	4 800	4 875	4 600	3 520	3 400	3 150
125	8 250	8 600	7 750	5 720	5 700	5 200

polarity-reversing switch to the sub-circuit, preferably of the unidirectional rotary type so that polarity is changed at every switching. A thermal starter is normally used.

Colours Available.—The standard range of colours is as follows :

Warm White, of exceptionally high efficiency and creamy appearance. The colour-rendering of this lamp is good, but red colours will not show in their proper strength and the lamp is therefore of doubtful value for domestic purposes though ideal for many industrial and commercial applications.

Daylight, nearly as efficient as the above, but whiter in appearance, blending well with natural daylight. Colour-rendering and applications similar to the above.

Natural, with rather better colour-rendering than either of the above, but not quite so efficient. Has a whitish appearance and is a very good lamp for general purposes where high efficiency and good colour are both important but neither is paramount. Often used in shops, offices, etc., and domestically in kitchens and bathrooms, also occasionally in living rooms.

Colour-matching, with superb colour-rendering very closely similar to that of cool north sky daylight. The very white effect produced may appear cold at low levels of illumination, but the coldness disappears when a fair quantity of light is used. Ideal for all purposes where true colour-rendering is required and frequently so used in drapers' shops, etc. A mixture of this light with an equal wattage of ordinary filament lamps has become very popular in shops, the fluorescent component providing liveliness and clarity of colour, the filament component the extra red for flattering complexions.

Warm Tone, having both colour appearance and colour-rendering very similar to ordinary filament lamps. Both types can therefore be used in the same room without any colour change being obvious. The *Warm Tone* lamp is mainly intended for social purposes, e.g. homes, hotels, restaurants and the like, but may also become popular in shops.

Operating Characteristics.—Fluorescent lamps emit about one-third as much total heat as filament lamps giving the same amount of light, but only about one-fifth as much radiated heat. They are therefore very suitable for locations such as showcases and temperature-controlled interiors where lack of heating effect may be important. Their light output varies by about 1 per cent. for each 1 per cent. change in mains voltage (compared with 4 per cent. variation in light of filament lamps). They give rated light output at normal room temperatures, output being reduced at temperatures much above or much below ; otherwise normal temperature variation has little effect. In general, light output after 5,000 hours' burning is about 70 per cent. of that at 100 hours.

A fault in some part of the circuit may often be traced by observing the following symptoms :

Lamp glows continuously at both ends, or one end, but makes no effort to start.—In the first case, faulty starter ; in the second, an earth in some part of the circuit and possibly a faulty starter also. With the instant-start circuit, lamp has no earthing strip, or earth is poor, or low mains voltage ; if glowing at one end only, faulty transformer or leads to " dead " end of the lamp short-circuited.

Lamp flashes repeatedly but cannot start.—Faulty starter giving insufficient pre-heating time ; or an old lamp. In the latter case one or both ends of the lamp may have become blackened and the lamp may light normally for a few moments, then die away with a shimmering effect.

Lamp lights normally but extinguishes after a few seconds, then repeats.—Probably abnormally low mains voltage. May also be due to faulty starter.

Swirling effect of light in lamp.—Probably disappears after a few switching operations on a new lamp. If it persists, change starter. If it still persists, renew lamp.

6-ft 85 W Fluorescent Tube.—Recently introduced is a 6-ft 85 W fluorescent tube available in white, warm white and natural. Its advantage over the 8 ft 85 W tube is its higher lumen output per foot length of tube. Design lumen levels are 5,700, 5,550 and 4,000 respectively for the 7,500-hour life.

Cold Cathode Fluorescent Tubes.—Another type of fluorescent tube—the cold cathode type—is now available. This type of lamp is usually made of 20-mm. tubing coated with fluorescent powder and with either a mercury and argon or neon filling. It is of the high-voltage type, operated from a step-up transformer and there is no delay period in switching on. A life of 10,000 hours or more may be expected and is unaffected by the frequency of switching. Mercury-filled tubes show the usual drop in efficiency throughout life, but that of neon-filled lamps remains constant. Both types remain alight with severe reductions in mains voltage, and can be dimmed by suitable apparatus.

Cold cathode lamps are manufactured in a wide range of standard colours including daylight, warm white, blue, green, gold and red. The colours can be used separately or mixed to give any desired result, the gold and red lamps being particularly useful for providing a warm-toned light. Dimming of one of mixed colours will provide a colour change. As the tubes can be manufactured in a variety of shapes and curves, they are suitable for decorative illumination in restaurants, theatres, etc., where the higher voltage required for operating them will not be objectionable.

New High-pressure Vapour Lamps

Two new types of lamps for street lighting are the h.p. sodium vapour and the h.p. mercury-metal iodide vapour lamps. The h.p.s.v. lamp has good colour rendering and high efficiency, e.g. the 400 W unit has a lighting design lumens of 36,000 for a life of 5,000 hr. The mercury-halogen 400 W lamp has a lighting design lumens of 22,000 for a life of 3,000 hr.

ULTRA-VIOLET LAMPS AND THEIR USES

IT is well known that white light when split into its components by means of a prism gives a visible spectrum ranging from dark red to violet. At the red end of the spectrum the radiations are of a much lower frequency (i.e. a greater wavelength) than the radiations which form the violet end of the spectrum. It has, for many years, been known that beyond the visible spectrum radiations of still higher frequencies occur. These radiations were grouped under the heading of ultra-violet rays. The best known method of detecting the presence of these rays is by means of certain substances such as fluorescent powders which glow or fluoresce under the activity of the rays.

It is now known that the ultra-violet section (i.e. the invisible portion of the spectrum) extends for an appreciable distance beyond the limit of the visible spectrum. That part of the u.v. spectrum which is near the visible spectrum is referred to as the near u.v. region. The next portion is known as the middle u.v. region and the third portion as the far u.v. region. "Near" u.v. rays are most effective for exciting fluorescence and it is these rays which contribute so largely to the efficiency of the modern fluorescent lamp. "Middle" u.v. rays are those which are most effective in therapeutics. "Far" u.v. rays have so far been applied chiefly in the destruction of germs, though they also have other applications in biology and medicine.

An improved type of ultra-violet generator has recently been produced. It is in the form of a mercury-vapour tube coated inside with a special type of fluorescent powder. The extremely short-wave u.v. radiations produced by the mercury vapour are largely converted into u.v. radiations of a greater wavelength. It is claimed that this unit, the "Rada" black-light generator, gives a total near u.v. output per watt of about three times that of the standard high-pressure mercury-vapour lamp. This new generator has a number of interesting applications. It can be used for the artificial ageing of coloured materials to test the fastness of dyes and it provides a highly efficient means for the fluorescent illumination of instrument panels and pointers in aircraft and ships. It also has applications for crack detection in ferrous and non-ferrous castings, for the identification of materials, and for the production of striking fluorescent advertisement signs and displays.

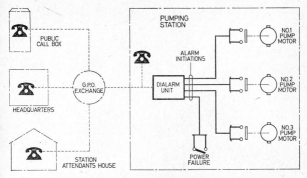

FIG. 1.—A Typical Dialarm Application.
(*Parkinson Cowan Ltd.*)

mains is available. Where no mains electricity is available, a primary battery power supply with a life expectancy of three years can be supplied.

A typical application is shown in Fig. 1. Alarms would be raised if any of the three pumps at the pumping station failed, or if there was a power failure. Dialarm can be arranged to call to, say, the headquarters and to the attendant's house, and should either or both not be in attendance, they can call Dialarm from any telephone to establish the current position at the pumping station.

Dialarm is housed, with its mains power supply, in a sealed steel case with wall-mounting straps. The dimensions are approximately 17 in. by 18 in. by 9 in. The primary and secondary battery power supplies are housed separately.

Telytalk System.—The Telytalk system, developed by Parkinson Cowan Measurement, is a versatile method for remote supervision and control over a normal G.P.O. subscriber telephone line. The instrument is situated at the remote outstation and connected to a telephone hand-set. It usually has an ex-directory telephone number allocated to it and when called from any other telephone on the G.P.O. network, it answers the call and gives a series of verbal messages which describe the different variables being monitored.

Each unit is custom-built to meet specific requirements

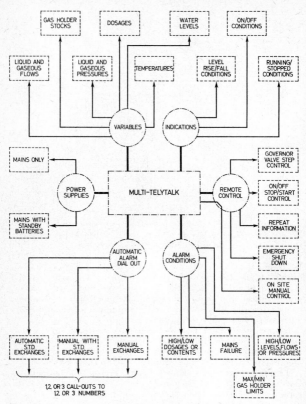

Fig. 2.—Some Common Applications for Remote Supervision and Control with Multi-Telytalk Equipment.
(*Parkinson Cowan Ltd.*)

and finds most applications for remote water pumping stations and unattended gas holder stations. When called, the equipment first gives its telephone number and location and identifies itself with an introductory announcement. Then a series of measurements follow in sequence covering all the variables being monitored. All the messages are stored on a prerecorded magnetic tape drum which contains up to 200 information channels on the standard unit. The variables are recorded along the drum in discreet bands, in ranges and increments specified to meet the site's requirements.

The variables are monitored by individual resistance transducers and each transmitter is examined in turn whenever the Telytalk is interrogated. The transmitting potentiometer forms one half of a Wheatstone bridge detector circuit. The variable play-back head which traverses the prerecorded drum unit is positioned by a servo-mechanism coupled to the feed-back potentiometer. As each transmitter is examined in turn, any error signal between the transmitting and feed-back potentiometers drives the servo-motor into the balance condition. The position of the play-back head at these points corresponds to the messages announcing the exact measured quantities which are being examined. The drum revolves after each balancing operation and the measurement is transmitted to the caller. The play-back head moves from one variable bank to the next, selecting the appropriate message within each band of variables.

The operations sequences are controlled by G.P.O. telephone relays circuitry whilst the A/F amplifiers and detector circuits are solid state. The messages are recorded with a track spacing of 0·050 in. and the resolution of the instrumentation is such that an accuracy of $\pm 0·5$ per cent is achieved over the traverse movement.

Remote control is effected simply by siting a small V/F tone transmitter at the supervisory office which connects to the caller's telephone. At predetermined points in the sequence the instrument invites the caller to control valves or pumps or adjust step-control flow rates etc. By depression of the key on his tone transmitter for three seconds at these various points, the caller can activate the necessary interposing relays to achieve the desired control function as required. Any number of control devices can in this way be operated in turn by the same controlling signal. In this way, if a repeat information facility at the end of the Telytalk scan is transmitted, the caller can obtain a complete re-examination of the conditions prevailing at the site—verifying that any

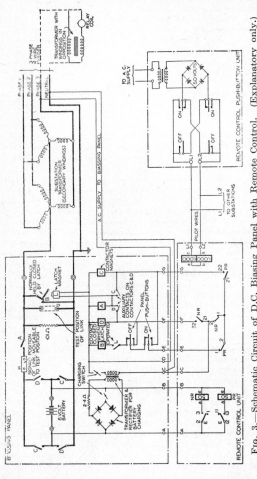

Fig. 3.—Schematic Circuit of D.C. Biasing Panel with Remote Control. (Explanatory only.)

(Standard Telephones & Cables, Ltd.)

EMERGENCY LIGHTING SYSTEM

EMERGENCY lighting systems can be divided into two categories, namely, installations where the emergency lighting is permanently illuminated (the *Continuous* system) and installations where the emergency lighting only comes on in the event of mains failure (the *Standby* system).

In the continuous arrangement the emergency load is normally supplied from the mains through a step-down transformer and is automatically transferred to the battery in the event of mains failure. In the standby scheme the emergency load is normally off but automatically comes into operation in the event of a mains failure.

The type of system selected is, in many cases, a matter of individual preference, but for certain buildings such as places of entertainment a continuous scheme is required by law.

However, when no regulations are involved and emergency lighting is being considered for the protection of personnel and/or property, e.g. in factories to protect work people from accidents in the event of a lighting failure with power supply to machines still available, or to prevent pilfering in shops or stores during a lighting failure, the standby scheme is used.

The Nife-Neverfayle series of emergency lighting equipment can be either of the standby or continuous type, or if required a combination of both. Standard equipments are available to deal with loads from 50 W at 12 V to 5·5 kW at 110 V.

The schemes are shown in Figs. 1 and 2 and the basic method of operation of the standby scheme is as follows :

1. The battery is normally standing on open-circuit.
2. The emergency lights are normally disconnected from the battery.
3. On an interruption in the mains supply or failure of the fuses, the contactor automatically connects the emergency lights to the battery.
4. When the mains supply is restored the battery is automatically disconnected from the load.
5. After an emergency discharge the battery is recharged by a taper charge circuit.
6. The charging circuit is automatically isolated if the contactor for any reason changes over to the battery with the charging supply still available.
7. Complete control of the equipment is effected by means of a four position master switch.

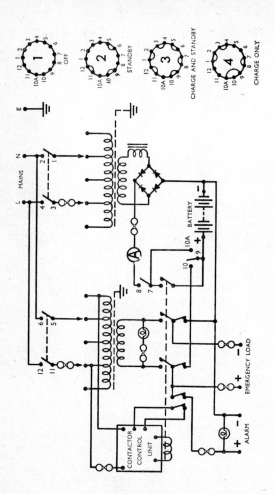

Fig. 1.—Continuous Emergency Lighting System.
(*Nife Batteries.*)

214

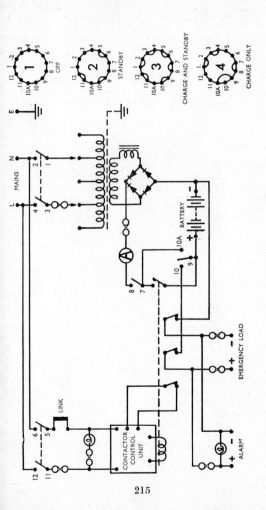

215

Fig. 2.—Standby Emergency Lighting Set.
(*Nife Batteries.*)

BATTERY CHARGING

MANY different types of battery chargers are now marketed. These comprise valve rectifiers, metal rectifiers, commutating rectifiers, motor generators, rotary transformers, lamp boards, resistance boards and mercury arc rectifiers. In addition, specialized battery chargers operating on the constant potential system are available, these chargers also involving the use of motor generators, commutating rectifiers or rotary transformers.

These different types of battery chargers can in principle be reduced to two methods, namely, the constant current method and the constant potential or constant voltage method.

Any consideration given to battery charging should be associated with the type of charging method to be adopted, and to enable the difference between the two methods and the characteristics of the various types of plant available to be appreciated, it is necessary firstly to consider the fundamental principles of battery charging as exemplified in the behaviour of the battery itself during charging and discharging.

The effect of passing a current into a battery is to cause a chemical change to take place. When a battery is charged the electrical energy is converted into chemical energy. A certain loss occurs in this transformation, this loss being indicated by the efficiency of the battery in the same way as with all other classes of electrical machinery.

It is shown on page 208, that the effect of the discharge current from a lead-acid cell is to convert the original lead peroxide on the positive plates and the pure lead on the negative plates to the same chemical substance, namely, lead sulphate. Since water is liberated the specific gravity of the acid will obviously be weakened during discharge.

The cell will continue to give a current until all the active material on both sides of plates is entirely converted to lead sulphate. In practice, however, the discharging of the cell is not taken to its extreme limit and a state of normal discharge is held to be reached only when a proportion of the material has been changed. During normal discharge the cell voltage will be from 2 to 2·1 volts. When the discharge continues beyond a certain point, the voltage will begin to drop rather suddenly, and immediately the voltage has reduced to a figure of 1·75 to 1·8, the cell is held to be discharged and to require recharging. The chemical action which takes place when the cell is recharged is the reverse of the action during discharging.

The practical evidence of the state of a cell lies in the variations which occur in the density of the acid, in the voltage of the cell, in its temperature, in the colour of the plates and in the gassing which takes place when the cell is fully charged. All these various indications are important.

In recharging the battery care must be taken not to exceed a safe value of charging at any time, or to continue the charging for too long a period, and a check must be made of the value of the voltage and specific gravity which will serve as an indication when the cell has been completely charged.

One of the most important changes which occurs is the variation of voltage, since this determines the whole principle of battery charging.

It has previously been stated that the voltage of a lead-acid cell when normally discharged is 1·8 volts. As the cell becomes charged and the active material converted from its discharged condition into its charged condition, the voltage of the cell will continuously rise until it reaches a value of approximately 2·5 to 2·7 volts on charge.

In view of the fact that the process of charging a battery consists of passing a current through it, the voltage applied to the battery must obviously be in excess of the voltage of the battery itself at any state of charge in order that a flow of current through the battery can be obtained. The voltage applied to the cell must be sufficiently in excess of the voltage of the cell itself, i.e. the back e.m.f., so that the difference divided by the resistance of the cell equals the charging current required.

In other words, the charging rate $= \dfrac{E_a - E_f}{R}$

where E_a = applied voltage,
   E_f = back e.m.f., and
   R = resistance of the cell.

Thus, assuming a single cell with discharge voltage of 1·8 and applied voltage of 2 volts and a cell resistance of 0·1 ohm, the charging current will be

$$\frac{2 - 1\cdot8}{0\cdot1} = 2 \text{ amperes.}$$

It will be obvious that as the back e.m.f. of the cell increases, the applied voltage must also increase in order to maintain the charging current. Thus, when the back e.m.f. of the cell reaches 2 volts, the applied voltage must be increased to 2·2 volts. This increase of charging voltage must continue until the cell is completely charged, by which time its voltage will be approximately 2·7 volts. In other words, for normal recharging we require a voltage of 2·7 volts for every cell we desire to charge in series.

The process of commercial recharging consists in the provision of efficient methods of charging all types and sizes of cells, both car and radio. It is essential to use direct current for battery charging and further it is essential—as will have been indicated by the foregoing—to provide a suitable value of d.c. voltage which will be in proportion to the number of cells to be charged.

In the case of direct current supplies, the commercial battery charger will, therefore, consist of means of reducing the mains d.c. voltage to a suitable value, and in the case of a.c. supplies it will be necessary to provide equipment which will firstly convert a.c. into d.c. and then provide the necessary value of d.c. voltage. The exact means by which this reduction and/or transformation is carried out distinguishes the various types of commercial battery charging equipment used in service.

For direct current supplies, the voltage can be reduced to a suitable value by means of lamps or resistances, or alternatively a motor driven from the d.c. mains drives the dynamo which generates a given value of d.c. output in amperes and volts. Since the supply system in the United Kingdom is a.c. the d.c. arrangement will be rare indeed.

In the case of alternating current supplies, we can use a motor generator or, alternatively, means of rectifying the current from a.c. to d.c., either by a rotary rectifier or by a static rectifier such as the oxide cathode, metal rectifier or mercury arc rectifier. In all instances, however, the final result is the same, i.e. the provision of a given d.c. voltage and current.

The exact type of battery charger used is of considerable commercial importance, since the design of the battery charger determines the cost and quality of recharging and the standard of the charging service which is given.

Constant Current System.—Since the maximum normal voltage of a fully charged cell is approximately 2·7 volts on charge, this value of voltage is necessary for each cell which it is required to charge in series. Thus, to charge 12 cells, the value of the applied voltage would be $12 \times 2 \cdot 7 = 32 \cdot 4$ volts. To charge 30 cells the applied voltage would be $30 \times 2 \cdot 7 = 81$ volts.

In the same way the number of cells which can be charged from a given d.c. voltage can be obtained by dividing the

218

D.C. CHARGING CIRCUITS

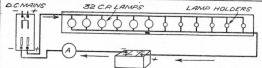

FIG. 1. DIAGRAM OF A TYPICAL LAMP RESISTANCE BOARD

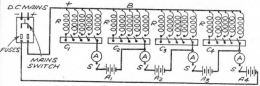

FIG. 2. DIAGRAM OF CASCADE RESISTANCES FOR CHARGING BATTERIES ON D.C. SUPPLY

RECTIFIER CHARGING CIRCUITS

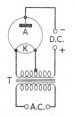

FIG. 3. SCHEMATIC DIAGRAM OF A SINGLE-PHASE HALF-WAVE RECTIFIER

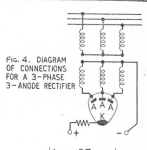

FIG. 4. DIAGRAM OF CONNECTIONS FOR A 3-PHASE 3-ANODE RECTIFIER

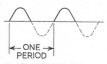

FIG. 5. SHOWING THE RESULTANT WAVE-FORM OBTAINED BY SINGLE-PHASE HALF-WAVE RECTIFICATION

FIG. 6. SHOWING THE WAVE-FORM OBTAINED FROM A 3-PHASE RECTIFIER

voltage by 2·7. A 100-volt d.c. circuit is capable of charging up to $\frac{100}{2·7} = 37$ cells.

In charging by this method, the cells are connected in series. The same value of current will flow through the complete series group. If cells which are variable in capacity have to be charged it will be necessary to connect them into a number of groups so that alternative values of charging current can be obtained.

The Construction of a Modern Charger.—For satisfactory service a modern battery charger should therefore preferably, consist of a number of charging circuits designed to give a variation of charging rates.

Adjustment of Charging Rate.—In order to obtain the correct value of charging current and to maintain this current at a constant rate it will be necessary to provide means on each charging circuit whereby the voltage applied to the cells on charge can be regulated firstly by the number of cells connected to the circuit, and secondly in accordance with their condition.

The best way of describing this feature is to take an example of, say, 12 2-volt cells to be charged at 3 amperes. The normal discharge voltage of 12 cells connected in series will be $12 \times 1·8 = 21·6$ volts.

Assuming the resistance of each cell as 0·1 ohm, the total resistance of the series group will be $12 \times 0·1 = 1·2$ ohms. Thus, to attain an initial charging current of 3 amperes the difference in voltage between the applied voltage and the back e.m.f. will be $3 \times 1·2$ (ohms × amperes in accordance with Ohm's law) = 3·6 volts.

The applied voltage would, therefore, need to be $21·6 + 3·6 = 25·2$ volts. Thus, according to the formula previously expressed, the charging current will be

$$\frac{E_a - E_f}{R} = \frac{25·2 - 21·6}{1·2} = \frac{3·6}{1·2} = 3 \text{ amperes.}$$

Immediately the cells begin to be charged the voltage will rise, and since this will reduce the difference between the applied voltage and the back E.M.F., the charging current will drop in proportion. In order to compensate for this the applied voltage must be increased. Thus, when the cell voltage is 2 volts per cell, i.e. total voltage $12 \times 2 = 24$ volts

PARALLEL CHARGING CIRCUITS

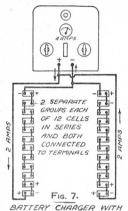

2 SEPARATE GROUPS EACH OF 12 CELLS IN SERIES AND BOTH CONNECTED TO TERMINALS

4 AMPS.

2 AMPS

2 AMPS

FIG. 7.

BATTERY CHARGER WITH AN OUTPUT OF 4 AMPS FITTED WITH ONLY ONE CHARGING CIRCUIT.

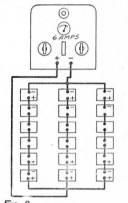

6 AMPS

FIG. 8. THREE GROUPS EACH OF SIX CELLS CONNECTED TO A 6-AMPERE SINGLE-CIRCUIT CHARGER.

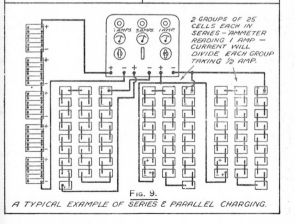

2 GROUPS OF 25 CELLS EACH IN SERIES — AMMETER READING 1 AMP — CURRENT WILL DIVIDE EACH GROUP TAKING ½ AMP.

2 AMPS. 3 AMPS. 1 AMP.

FIG. 9.

A TYPICAL EXAMPLE OF SERIES & PARALLEL CHARGING.

the applied voltage must be increased to a value 3·6 volts in **excess** of this voltage, namely, 27·6 volts.

At all times until the cells are completely charged the applied voltage must be sufficiently in excess of the variable back e.m.f. in order to provide the required constant charging current.

Charging Resistances.—The way in which this variation of applied voltage is obtained is by the use of charging resistances. In the above example the normal voltage of the charger is 30 volts. In order to begin charging we require an applied voltage of only 25·2 volts. We therefore provide a charging resistance of sufficient value to reduce the 30 volts to 25·2 volts, and by making the resistance variable we can reduce the amount of resistance and thereby reduce the voltage drop until, when all cells are charged, the resistance is entirely cut out.

Handling Various Sizes of Cells.—The difficulty which sometimes exists is that there may be a rather awkward variation in the number of cells to be charged. Let us assume that we require to charge the following :—

1. Three 12-volt car batteries (18 cells) at 5 amperes.
2. 20 radio cells at 3 amperes.
3. 28 radio cells at 1 ampere.

The maximum number of cells is 28, and therefore the maximum voltage of the charging plant will need to be $28 \times 2 \cdot 7 = 75 \cdot 6$. In practice it will be preferable to use a 75-volt plant which is standard. A suitable plant would, therefore, be a charger with three circuits, giving charging rates of 5 amperes, 3 amperes and 1 ampere respectively.

When it is necessary to convert from a.c. to d.c. there are several commercial methods available, namely motor generators, commutating rectifiers, metal rectifiers and valve rectifiers as mentioned earlier.

A motor generator comprises an a.c. motor driving a d.c. generator. The generator is designed to have the requisite value of voltage and current output determined by the size and number of the batteries to be charged.

In the case of commutating rectifiers and metal and valve rectifiers, a different principle is adopted. The actual incoming a.c. supply is converted from a current which continuously reverses into a current which flows in one direction only and thereby becomes suitable for battery charging. In his instance the current wave will contain a ripple, its magnitude depending on the number of the phases.

The Metal Rectifier.—See p. 141.

Constant-potential System.—In constant potential charging, a constant voltage is applied, and the charging current will vary according to the state of charge of the battery. Motor generators or commutating rectifiers are used, and are usually designed to give a constant $7\frac{1}{2}$ or 15 volts and a comparatively large current output to copper busbars.

The batteries to be charged are connected in 6- or 12-volt units across the positive and negative busbars. Some sets have three busbars, giving two voltages, $7\frac{1}{2}$ across the centre and either of the two outer busbars, and 15 across the two outers.

When the battery is first connected, a high charging current flows, but as the terminal voltage of the battery rises (as the battery becomes charged), the charging current drops automatically. At the end of the charge, the voltage of the battery will be equal to the voltage of the busbars, and, consequently, no current will flow.

If a battery is badly run down, or unhealthy, it is desirable to provide connecting leads incorporating a sufficient amount of resistance to reduce the initial current to a suitable value, which in practice is 10 or 20 amps., depending upon the ampere-hour rating of the battery.

SMALL GENERATING PLANTS

THE nationalization of the public supply in 1948 has tende
to retard the installation of private generating plants excep
at two rather opposite ends of the scale. These are th
small private plant for use in country districts where th
public supply is not available or is not economical, and th
larger power-plants installed at factories or refineries, whe
the load is so great, or where continuity of supply is vita
that a self-contained plant is desirable.

The small generating plant is generally driven by a Diese
engine, although the free-piston engine is proving qui
popular. The Diesel engine, working on oil, has an econom
efficiency that enables it to compete with the public suppl
and it is now the standard method of generating electricit
except in the case of very small or very large plants.

The smallest Diesel set made commercially gives about
kilowatt, but up to 3 or 4 kilowatts the petrol engine is
competitor. Over this and up to units of 1 000 kilowat
the Diesel engine is used. For very large plants of sever
thousand kilowatts the modern steam plant is still the mo
economical.

Small generating plants of from 300 watts to 50 kilowat
have now reached a very advanced stage of developmer
and include a fair amount of automatic control.

Non-automatic Plants.—These are usually battery plan
run for a few hours each day to charge the battery whic
supplies the load at all times. Both Diesel and petrol engin
are used and starting may be by hand or from the batter
The size of plant must be fixed so that the battery will supp
the maximum load likely to be required over a period of at lea
48 hours so that charging is not required every day. Th
engine size will be controlled to some extent by the batter
as charging must be at the 8- or 10-hour rate.

A typical country house plant is as follows :

Normal full load—lamps, etc., totalling 1500 watts.
Estimated maximum watt-hours in 48 hours—20,000.
Total battery capacity—90 per cent efficiency—22,200 watt-hour
Details of battery—60 cells of 200 ampere-hour capacity.
Maximum charging rate—10-hour rate—20 amps.
Output of generator—22 amps. at 110 to 170 volts.
Kilowatt rating—3,750 watts—4 kilowatts approx.
Engine required—double kilowatt output—10 h.p.

In actual practice it would be found that under ordinary circumstances the above plant would run satisfactorily if the battery is charged up two or three times per week, and in the summer the engine would be available for a whole week for inspection and overhaul if necessary.

Fully Automatic Plants.—As an alternative to the battery plant, fully automatic plants can be obtained which supply the load direct from the generator. These plants always start up automatically and a small starting battery is used for this purpose. A typical example of this is the Kohler system, which uses a large car type battery for starting up the plant.

As soon as a switch is closed this starting battery automatically closes contactors which connect it to a special winding on the generator, thus starting the engine. The plant continues to run until all load is switched off, when it shuts down. The starting battery is charged up while the engine is running. This system is used for plants from a few hundred watts to units giving 20 or 30 kilowatts.

Floating Battery Sets.—A modification of the fully automatic set as described above is that where a small capacity battery is used with automatic operation. In this case a battery (of full line voltage) is used to carry small loads of one to ten lamps. The control gear is arranged so that as soon as the load exceeds a certain value (from $\frac{1}{10}$ to $\frac{1}{4}$ of normal full load) the engine is automatically started by the floating battery and the whole of the load is then supplied by the engine until it reaches the maximum output of the set. In some cases, should the load be more than this, the balance is then supplied by the battery.

These sets are fully automatic and do not need any regular attention except for seeing to the supply of fuel and oil and the usual attention to both engine and battery. The automatic control ensures that the battery is always kept in a charged condition.

Apart from the floating battery system as outlined above, plants with a full-size battery are also now entirely automatic, and these are arranged for the load to be taken from the battery only or from both the battery and the engine as required.

Voltage and Supply.—As it is desirable to keep the number of cells fairly low, plants using a main or floating

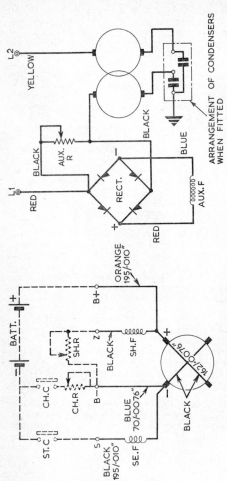

FIG. 1.—Circuit Diagram of 2·5 kVA Generating Set.

A typical example of a self-exciting alternator using a current transformer and rectifier as a compensated voltage regulator; a voltage regulation from no-load to full-load of ± 2½ per cent is obtained. This alternator is fitted with series starting turns to enable the machine to be rotated, by a current supplied from the battery, in order to provide push-button electric starting. The battery charging supply is taken from the exciter side of the alternator.

Nevage Lyon Ltd.

Abbreviations: Batt—Battery: ST C—Starter contactor: CH C—Charge contactor: CH R—Charge resistance: SH R—Shunt resistance: SH F—Shunt field: SE F—Series start winding: CT—Current transformer:

226

battery are usually either 50 or 110 volts, and of course d.c. has to be used. Above 5 kilowatts, 220 or 240 volts can be used and where economical this voltage is an advantage from the point of view of any change-over to public supply at a future date.

With fully automatic plants using only a starting battery any voltage can be used, and in this case a.c. can be generated. (A rectifier is used to charge the starting battery.) For the very small sets d.c. is still more practicable, but a.c. sets have been developed very successfully for emergency use in case of failure of the public supply.

Composite Plants and Stand-by.—Where the main load is supplied by the engine it is desirable to have a stand-by plant, and there is also the question of widely varying load. Both these points are met by installing two plants of either the same or different outputs. For example, if the load occasionally amounts to 10 kilowatts, either two 6-kilowatt plants or one 4- and one 7-kilowatt plant could be put down.

In either case one engine starts up first and the second comes into operation as soon as the load is larger than can be handled by one engine. With the small and large plant a further arrangement is that the small plant runs for low loads, and if it increases further the load is transferred to the large plant, the small plant coming in again later if required. With either scheme a limited supply is available should one engine fail or be under repair.

ELECTRIC MOTORS

D.C. MOTORS

D.C. MOTORS are divided into three classes, as follows :

(1) *The series-wound motor,* in which the field is in series with the armature. This type of motor is only used for direct coupling and other work where the load (or part of the load) is permanently coupled to the motor. This will be seen from the speed-torque characteristic, which shows that on no load or light load the speed will be very high and therefore dangerous.

(2) *The shunt-wound motor.*—In this case the field is in parallel with the armature, as shown in the diagram, and the shunt motor is the standard type of d.c. motor for ordinary purposes. Its speed is nearly constant, falling off as the load increases due to resistance drop and armature reaction.

(3) *The compound-wound motor,* which is a combination of the two. There is a series winding in series with the armature and a shunt winding in parallel with it. The relative proportion of the field and series winding can be varied in order to make the characteristics nearer those of the series motor or those of the shunt-wound motor. The typical speed-torque curve is shown in the diagram.

Compound-wound motors are used for cranes and other heavy duty where an overload may have to be carried and a heavy starting torque is required.

Speed Control.—Speed control is obtained as follows:

Series motors, by series resistance in parallel with the field winding of the motor. The resistance is then known as a diverter resistance. Another method used in traction consists of starting up two motors in series and then connecting them in parallel when a certain speed has been reached. Series resistances are used to limit the current in this case.

Shunt- and Compound-wound Motors.—Speed regulation on shunt- and compound-wound motors is obtained by resistance in series with the shunt-field winding only. This is shown diagrammatically for a shunt motor in Fig. 4.

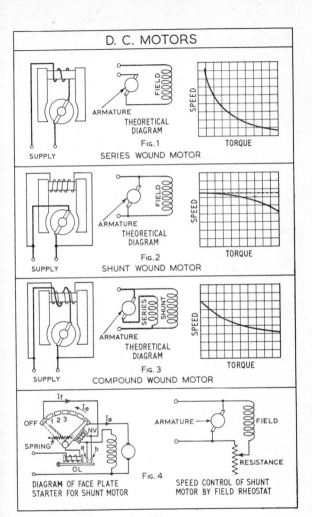

D. C. MOTORS

ARMATURE   FIELD
THEORETICAL
DIAGRAM
FIG. 1
SUPPLY   SERIES WOUND MOTOR

SPEED / TORQUE

ARMATURE   FIELD
THEORETICAL
DIAGRAM
FIG. 2
SUPPLY   SHUNT WOUND MOTOR

SPEED / TORQUE

ARMATURE   SERIES   SHUNT
THEORETICAL
DIAGRAM
FIG. 3
SUPPLY   COMPOUND WOUND MOTOR

SPEED / TORQUE

If   Ie
OFF   1 2 3   Ia
NV
SPRING
a b
OL
DIAGRAM OF FACE PLATE
STARTER FOR SHUNT MOTOR

ARMATURE   FIELD
RESISTANCE
FIG. 4
SPEED CONTROL OF SHUNT
MOTOR BY FIELD RHEOSTAT

Starting.—The principle of starting a shunt motor will be seen from Fig. 4 which shows the face-plate type starter, the starting resistance being in between the segments marked 1, 2, 3, etc.

The starting-handle is held in position by the no-volt coil, marked NV, which automatically allows the starter to return to the off position if the supply fails. Overload protection is obtained by means of the overload coil, marked OL, which on overload short circuits the no-volt coil by means of the contact marked a and b.

When starting a shunt-wound motor it is most important to see that the shunt rheostat (or speed control) is in the slow-speed position. This is because the starting torque is proportional to the field current and this field current must be at its maximum value for starting purposes. Many starters have the speed regulator interlocked with the starting-handle so that the motor cannot be started with a weak field.

Ward-Leonard Control.—One of the most important methods of speed control is that involving the Ward-Leonard principle which comprises a d.c. motor fed from its own motor-generator set. The diagram of connections is shown in Fig. 5. The usual components are an a.c. induction or synchronous motor, driving a d.c. generator, and a constant voltage exciter; a shunt-wound d.c. driving motor and a field rheostat. The speed of the driving motor is controlled by varying the applied voltage, by means of the rheostat in the shunt winding circuit of the generator. The d.c. supply

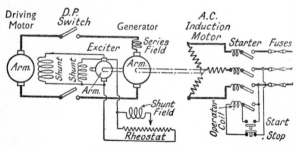

Fig. 5.—Ward-Leonard Control.

to the field windings of the generator and driving motor is obtained by means of an exciter driven from the generator shaft.

With this equipment it is possible to obtain 10 to 1 speed range by regulation of the generator shunt field and these sets have been used for outputs of $\frac{1}{2}$ h.p. and upwards. On the smaller sizes speed ranges up to 15 to 1 have been obtained, but for general purposes the safe limit can be taken as 10 to 1. Speed control obtained in this way is extremely stable and the speed regulation between no load and full load at any particular setting is from 7 to 10 per cent, depending on the size and design of the equipment.

This type of drive has been used for a variety of industrial applications and has been particularly successful in the case of electric planers and certain types of lifts, with outputs varying from 20 to 150 h.p., also in the case of grinders in outputs of $\frac{1}{2}$, 1, and 2 h.p., with speed ranges from 6 : 1 to 10 : 1.

A.C. MOTORS

ALTERNATING current motors can be grouped as follows :

    (a) Induction motors.
    (b) Synchronous motors.
    (c) Variable-speed commutator motors including the Schrage motor.
    (d) Series motors.
    (e) Single phase repulsion, capacitor and shunt motors.
    (f) Pole-changing and other special motors.

The first three are used in all sizes, and for all general purposes induction motors are employed on account of their simplicity, reliability and low first cost. Synchronous motors are generally installed where it is desirable to obtain power-factor improvement or where a constant speed is required. They are only economical in the case of loads of 50 h.p. and over, although there are instances where smaller machines are in use for special purposes.

The three-phase commutator motor until recently has been the only a.c. motor for large outputs which gives full speed control, and although expensive it is being used for duties where variable speed is required. Pole-changing and other special motors with speed control characteristics are now becoming available and brief details of them are given later on in this chapter.

Groups (d) and (e) represent the types used for small or fractional h.p. motors, which also include induction motors. These small motors have been developed to a great extent because of the number of small machines incorporating individual drive. Normally fractional h.p. motors include machines developing from $\frac{1}{40}$ h.p. to about 2 h.p., although this latter size appears not to fit in with the term fractional h.p. The reason for its inclusion is that a different technique is used for manufacturing small motors which are turned out in large quantities by mass-production methods. Most of the manufacturers of these small motors can supply them with gearing incorporated giving final shaft speed of any value down to one revolution in 24 hours or even longer.

The induction motor, which can be termed the standard motor, is now made on mass production lines, and as a result of the standardization of voltage and frequency, the cost of standard-sized new motors is exceptionally low. The absence of a commutator and, in the case of the squirrel-cage motor, of any connection whatever to the rotor, combined with the simplicity of starting, make it the most reliable and the cheapest form of power-drive available.

There are a number of specialized motors which are used in a few unusual applications, but these will not be described as they are really rather of academic interest than of general use in industry. The linear induction motor falls within this category although this has been applied to overhead cranes and as a means of actuation where force without movement is required.

The use of synchronous motors for improvement of power factor is referred to in the section dealing with power factor, but it should be realized that the essential points of a synchronous motor are its constant speed (depending on the frequency) and the fact that the power factor at which it operates can be varied at will over a certain range—usually from 0·6 leading to 0·8 lagging—this being accomplished by varying the exciting current

THE INDUCTION MOTOR

THE essential principle of an induction motor is that the current in the stator winding produces a rotating flux which because it cuts the rotor bars induces a current in the winding of the rotor. This current then produces its own field which reacts with the rotating stator flux thus producing the necessary starting and running torque.

The stator winding to produce this rotating flux is fairly simple in the case of a three-phase motor, being based on three symmetrical windings, as shown in Fig. 6. In the case of single-phase and the now vanishing two-phase it is not quite so easily understood.

The stator field will revolve at synchronous speed and if no power whatever was required to turn the rotor it would catch up with the flux and would also revolve at synchronous speed. The condition for torque production would then have vanished. As, however, a certain amount of power is required to turn the rotor even if unconnected to any load, the speed is always slightly less than synchronous. As the load increases the speed falls in order to allow the additional rotor currents to be induced to give a larger torque.

The difference between the actual speed and synchronous speed is termed the *slip*, which is usually expressed as a percentage or a fraction of the synchronous speed. For standard machines the maximum slip at full load is usually about 4 per cent.

Calculation of Synchronous Speed.—Induction motors are made with any number of poles (in multiples of 2), but it is not usual to make motors with more than 10 poles, and for ordinary use 2, 4 and 6 poles are chosen, if possible, on account of the lower first cost and higher efficiency.

$$\text{Synchronous speed in r.p.m.} = \frac{\text{frequency} \times 60}{\text{number of pairs of poles}}.$$

Thus a 2-pole motor on 50 cycles will have a synchronous speed of 3,000 r.p.m., a 4-pole 1,500 r.p.m., and a 6-pole 1,000 r.p.m. The suitability of 1,500 r.p.m. for many purposes has made the 4-pole motor the more usual.

The actual rotor speed for 4 per cent slip is given for various motors on 50 cycles in the table on page 248. Slip is calculated from

$$\text{percentage slip} = \frac{(\text{syn. speed} - \text{rotor speed}) \times 100}{\text{syn. speed}},$$

THE INDUCTION MOTOR

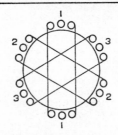

FIG. 6. THREE - PHASE STATOR WINDING
TO PRODUCE ROTATING FIELD

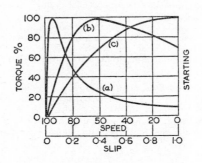

FIG. 7. TORQUE – SLIP CURVES

(A) = NO ADDED RESISTANCE IN ROTOR   R = 1
  (B) = WITH ADDED RESISTANCE   R = 4
(C) = WITH MORE ADDED RESISTANCE   R = 20

STARTING INDUCTION MOTORS

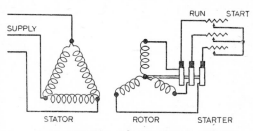

SUPPLY

RUN   START

STATOR   ROTOR   STARTER

FIG. 8. STARTING WOUND-ROTOR MOTOR

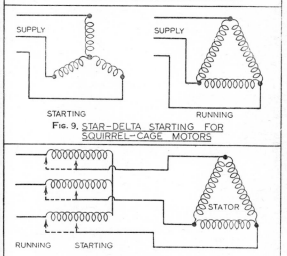

SUPPLY   SUPPLY

STARTING   RUNNING

FIG. 9. STAR-DELTA STARTING FOR
SQUIRREL-CAGE MOTORS

STATOR

RUNNING   STARTING

FIG. 9A. AUTO-TRANSFORMER STARTING
FOR SQUIRREL-CAGE MOTORS

and the rotor speed for any given slip will be

$$\text{rotor speed} = \text{syn. speed}\left(\frac{100 - \text{slip}}{100}\right),$$

the slip being the percentage slip.

Variation of Slip with Torque.—It can be shown that the torque of an induction motor is proportional to

$$T = \frac{kE_2 s R_2}{R_2{}^2 + (s X_2)^2}$$

where T = torque
  k = constant
  E_2 = rotor voltage
  s = fractional slip
  R_2 = rotor resistance
  X_2 = rotor reactance.

The variation of slip with torque can therefore be calculated and typical torque-slip curves are given in Fig. 7. These curves are for the same motor, and curve (a) is for the rotor short-circuited, whereas (b) and (c) are for cases where additional or added resistance has been put in the rotor circuit. It will be seen from these curves and also from the formula above that the torque at starting or low speeds is greatly increased by adding resistance in the rotor circuit, and this principle is made use of in the wound-rotor induction motor which is used to start up against heavy loads.

It can also be shown that maximum torque occurs when $R_2 = s X_2$ when the slip will be $s = \dfrac{R_2}{X_2}$.

Wound-rotor or Slip-ring Motor.—The slip-ring induction motor is used for duties where the motor has to start up against a fairly heavy load and the slip-rings are arranged for added resistance to be inserted in the rotor circuit for starting purposes. The diagram in Fig. 8 shows how the various circuits are connected to the supply and to the variable rotor resistance.

This type of motor is referred to as a *wound-rotor* motor, because for this purpose the rotor has to be wound with insulated conductors similar to those used for the stator. In the case of larger motors, an arrangement is fitted to the rotor shaft enabling the slip-rings to be short-circuited and the brushes lifted off the slip-rings, thus reducing both electrical and friction losses. Starters for these motors are described in the section on *Motor Starters*.

Auto-Transformer Starting.—The use of an auto-transformer is confined to those cases where a definite limit is required to the starting current, and the arrangement is shown in Fig. 9A, the transformer being disconnected from the supply in the running position. Transformer tappings enable the starting voltage to be selected to obtain the starting torque required for the load. Starting torque and current are each equal to the square of the transformer tapping (fraction) × direct switching value; e.g. 50 per cent tapping gives $(\frac{1}{2})^2$ or 25 per cent of the direct switching value.

Primary Resistance Starting.*—In this method of reduced voltage starting, the stator is connected through an adjustable three-phase series resistance. As the motor accelerates, the resistance is short-circuited in one or several steps. A heavier line current is required for a certain starting torque compared with other methods, e.g. 50 per cent line voltage and current gives 25 per cent torque, and 80 per cent line voltage and current gives 64 per cent torque. Heavy peak currents are avoided. The number of starts is limited by the resistance rating. When high torque motors are employed, this method shows appreciable saving in first cost, and the simple yet robust construction will give very low maintenance costs. If it is not important to strictly limit the starting current, these advantages recommend its more extended use, and in an emergency or breakdown, the method allows considerable scope for ingenious improvisation.

Squirrel-Cage versus Slip-ring.—A slip-ring motor may be chosen for a particular application in preference to a squirrel-cage machine for one or more of several reasons :

(1) To limit the starting current drawn from the line.
(2) To obtain a high value of starting torque for a comparatively low current drawn from the line.
(3) To obtain speed control.

If a squirrel-cage motor can be used that will satisfy either (1) or (2) for a particular duty, it will be possible to dispense with the slip-ring machine on that particular score. Both the starting torque and starting current of squirrel-cage motors depend on the characteristics of the rotor employed ; and there is a wide choice of motor for different types of drive.

* From a Paper by S. H. Harding, M.I.E.E., read before the Association of Supervising Electrical Engineers.

"High Resistance" Squirrel-Cage Motor.—As with the slip-ring motor, the starting torque of the motor can be increased by using a rotor with a higher resistance; but since this resistance has to remain permanently in circuit (in the ordinary squirrel-cage motor), it cannot be great if the motor is to retain anything like normal efficiency. A "high resistance" rotor has been used in applications such as forge hammers and power presses. The motor is allowed to slow down with increasing load so that the stored energy of the flywheel and other moving parts of the system may be utilized to relieve the motor of very heavy overloads. By this means also the supply line is relieved of very heavy peak currents, since the additional peak torque is provided by the flywheel and not by the motor. With such machines, therefore, since the load is of an intermittent nature, efficiency is not of so great importance as overload capacity.

High-resistance rotors have been frequently used on cranes and hoists where a high starting torque is required, but generally it may be said that, unless there is some definite advantage to be gained, the inefficiency will be such as to preclude their use in any situation where consumption is of importance.

Double Squirrel-Cage High Torque Motor.—In order to overcome the disadvantages of the squirrel-cage motor, and avoid having to use the more expensive slip-ring motor and its associated gear, increasing attention has been given to the use of the double squirrel-cage in which the resistance of the squirrel-cage rotor is increased temporarily while starting.

The double squirrel-cage rotor in its most simple form consists of two separate squirrel cages. The outer or starting cage is made of high-resistance material and is arranged to have the smallest possible reactance. The inner cage is of the ordinary low-resistance type, generally consisting of copper bars and rings, and since it is sunk deep into the iron, has a high reactance. The four qualities—reactance and resistance of inner and outer cages—can be varied in an infinite number of combinations and many different shapes of speed-torque curve can be obtained.

At starting, the frequency of the currents in the rotor conductors is the same as the supply frequency, thus the high reactance of the inner cage produces a choking effect and reduces the current flowing in this winding. The outer cage, being of high resistance, develops a high starting torque

242

depending largely on the value of its resistance. As the rotor accelerates and approaches synchronism, the frequency of the e.m.f.s in its conductors falls and the choking effect in the inner cage is reduced ; the inner cage now carries practically all the current until finally, when near synchronism, the rotor operates with the characteristics of an ordinary low resistance rotor. The general result is to produce a machine having a high starting torque and a high running efficiency, with reasonably small values of starting current.

Often the higher starting torque allows the motor to be started on reduced voltage provided the load against which it is required to accelerate is not too great.

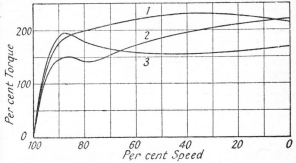

Fig. 14.—Torque-speed Curves of Various Double Squirrel-Cage Motors.

By altering the relative values of resistance and reactance, a wide variety of torque-speed characteristics can be obtained (Fig. 14). For example, one make of standard high torque motors available up to about 75 h.p. for direct switching develops at least twice full-load torque at standstill and takes a starting current of about 350 per cent full load current. In another range of standard machines for star-delta starting, 100 per cent of full load torque is developed at starting in the star connection, the starting current being 150–175 per cent full load current.

It should be noted that the cost of double squirrel-cage machine and its starting gear is considerably less than an equivalent slip-ring motor with resistance starter, and performance is obtained without sacrifice of running efficiency.

Extra High-speed Induction Motors.—Certain types of wood- and metal-working machines and portable tools require very high speeds of rotation (e.g. up to 27,000 r.p.m.). Such speeds cannot be obtained with a direct drive from an ordinary induction motor supplied at standard frequency (50 cycles), as the maximum speed is 3,000 r.p.m. (corresponding to two poles). In these special cases, where a direct drive is particularly advantageous, the only solution to the problem is to raise the frequency of the supply to the motor. This is accomplished by means of a frequency changer set, or frequency booster.

A frequency booster is a slip-ring induction machine similar in construction to a slip-ring induction motor. If this is excited from the A.C. mains and driven in the opposite direction to that of the rotating magnetic field of its primary winding, a high-frequency supply can be drawn from the secondary winding.

Either the stator or rotor can be made the primary, selection being according to whichever best suits the actual requirements.

The frequency booster may be driven by a motor (direct or belt coupled) or by any other source of mechanical power.

With different driving-motor speeds and excitation windings, different frequencies can be generated, as indicated by the following formula:

High-frequency output

$$= \left(\text{Pairs of poles in booster} \times \frac{\text{r.p.m. of motor}}{60} \right)$$
$$+ \text{Excitation frequency.}$$

Special precautions are necessary in the arrangement of the switchgear. The driving motor starting switches must be interlocked with the switches controlling the power supply of the induction machine stator and rotor, so that it is impossible to connect either the input or the output of the high-frequency unit before the machines are run up to speed. Similarly, it must be arranged so that in the event of the motor circuit being tripped the input and output circuits of the booster are tripped at the same time.

The standard high-frequency portable electric tool is designed to operate at 200 cycles per second. Compared with the " universal " type of motor, the speed does not drop in accordance with the load applied, and there are no commutators or brushes to wear or to be replaced.

FULL LOAD CURRENTS OF ALTERNATING CURRENT MOTORS

The values given below may vary slightly with different types of motors but can be accepted as reasonably accurate.

In Amperes.

B.H.P.	Single Phase										Two Phase		Three Phase					
	Split Phase					Capacitor												
	Volts					Volts					Volts		Volts					
	100	200	230	400	480	100	200	230	400	480	200	400	200	220	350	400	440	500
1	12·9	6·5	5·6	3·2	2·7	11·6	5·9	5·1	2·9	2·4	2·9	1·4	3·4	3·1	2	1·7	1·5	1·4
2	24	12	10·4	6	5	22	11	9·5	5·4	4·5	5·7	2·9	6	6	3·8	3·3	3·3	2·6
3	35	17	15	9	7	31	15	13	7·8	6·5	8·4	4·2	9·8	8·9	5·7	4·9	4·5	3·9
4	45	23	20	11	9·4	40	20	18	10	8·5	11	5·6	13	12	7·5	6·5	6	5·2
5	56	28	25	14	11	51	25	22	13	11	14	6·8	16	14	9·1	7·9	7	6·3
6	66	33	29	17	14	60	29	26	15	13	16	8·1	19	17	11	9·4	8·2	7·5
7½	82	41	36	21	17	74	37	33	19	16	20	10	24	21	14	12	11·5	9·4
8	87	43	38	22	18	78	39	34	20	16	21	11	25	22	15	13	12	9·8
10	109	54	47	27	23	98	48	42	24	20	26	13	30	27	17	15	14	12
15	159	79	69	40	33	147	73	64	37	31	38	19	44	40	26	22	20	18
20	209	105	91	52	44	193	97	84	48	41	50	25	58	53	34	29	26	23
25	256	128	111	64	53	237	118	103	59	49	62	31	72	66	42	36	33	29
30	306	152	134	77	64	283	142	124	71	59	74	37	86	78	50	43	39	34
40	400	200	174	100	83	370	185	161	93	77	96	48	111	101	64	56	51	45
50	487	244	212	122	102	450	226	196	113	94	118	59	137	124	79	68	62	55
60	586	292	254	147	122	542	270	235	136	113	140	70	162	147	94	81	74	65
75	715	358	310	179	150	662	330	287	166	139	171	86	198	180	114	99	90	79
100	941	471	410	235	196	870	435	380	217	182	228	114	263	239	152	132	120	105
150	—	—	—	—	—	—	—	—	—	—	336	168	388	356	225	194	176	155
200	—	—	—	—	—	—	—	—	—	—	446	223	517	468	299	258	235	207

The current required for any alternating current motor can be obtained from the following equations. The power factor and efficiency can be obtained from the table given on page 248.

Single Phase

$$\text{Current} = \frac{\text{Horse-power} \times 746}{\text{Voltage} \times \text{Power Factor} \times \text{Efficiency}}$$

Three Phase

$$\text{Current} = \frac{\text{Horse-power} \times 746}{1\cdot732 \times \text{Line Voltage} \times \text{Power Factor} \times \text{Efficiency}}$$

Two Phase, four-wire supply

$$\text{Current} = \frac{\text{Horse-power} \times 746}{2 \times \text{Line Voltage} \times \text{Power Factor} \times \text{Efficiency}}$$

Two Phase, three-wire supply

Current = In Outers, as above.

In Common, $1\cdot414 \times$ Outer Value

SYNCHRONOUS MOTORS

THE synchronous motor is essentially a reversed alternator and is specifically used for power-factor correction. As its name implies, it has a constant speed (running at synchronous speed at all loads), and its power factor can be controlled by varying the exciting current. It can thus be made to take a leading current for power-factor improvement purposes. The synchronous motor itself is not self-starting and it must also be synchronized on to the supply when it has been run up to speed by a special starting motor or by some other means.

"**Straight**" **Self-contained Motor.**—Refer to Fig. 15, which shows the arrangement of a self-contained synchronous motor suitable for driving a steady load but does not show any method of starting. The three-phase supply is taken direct to the stator and a d.c. supply is necessary for excitation. This can either be obtained from a separate d.c. system (sometimes used where there are several motors in use) or from the individual exciter mounted direct to the motor as shown. Power-factor control is obtained by varying the excitation—this being controlled in large motors by means of a rheostat in the field circuit of the exciter.

This type of motor in its simple form has no starting torque and will not therefore start up under load. Also if the over-load capacity is exceeded the motor will fall "out of step" and will shut down. It must then be started up and synchronized in the usual manner.

Synchronous-Induction Motor.—The diagram for a typical self-starting synchronous-induction motor is shown in Fig. 16. It will be seen that by means of a starting resistance the machine will start up as an induction motor. As full speed is reached the motor will pull into synchronism (against full load if required) and the starting resistances are then short-circuited.

A two-phase winding is used on the rotor and arranged so that the neutral point is used as one connection for the excitation circuit.

Hunting.—One of the features of a synchronous motor is that on a fluctuating load it may *hunt*.

In modern industrial motors this is prevented by means of a damping winding in which eddy currents are induced by the variations in speed should hunting occur.

Hunting is more likely to occur with weak excitation than with strong. Temporary hunting can therefore often be cured by strengthening the field.

SYNCHRONOUS MOTORS

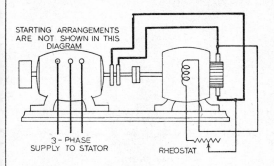

STARTING ARRANGEMENTS
ARE NOT SHOWN IN THIS
DIAGRAM

3 - PHASE
SUPPLY TO STATOR

RHEOSTAT

FIG. 15. MOTOR WITH EXCITER

POWER FACTOR IS CONTROLLED BY RHEOSTAT IN
EXCITING CIRCUIT OF EXCITER

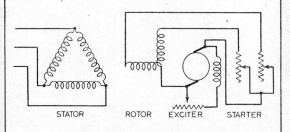

STATOR   ROTOR   EXCITER   STARTER

FIG. 16. SYNCHRONOUS INDUCTION MOTOR

A TWO-PHASE ROTOR IS USED. DIAGRAM SHOWS
METHOD OF STARTING AS AN INDUCTION MOTOR

247

SYNCHRONOUS SPEED

No. of Poles on Stator.	Synchronous speed on 50 ~ r.p.m.	Rotor Speed at 4 per cent Slip.
2	3,000	2,880
4	1,500	1,440
6	1,000	960
8	750	720
10	600	576

EFFICIENCY AND POWER FACTOR OF 4-POLE INDUCTION MOTORS ON 50 CYCLES

The following are average values for standard motors running at 1,440 to 1,470 r.p.m.

FULL LOAD

H.P.	Efficiency.				Power Factor.			
	Single Phase.		Two Phase.	Three Phase.	Single Phase.		Two Phase.	Three Phase.
	Split Phase.	Capacitor.			Split Phase.	Capacitor.		
	Per cent.	Per cent.	Per cent.	Per cent.	Per cent.	Per cent.	Per cent.	Per cent.
1	65	70	73	74	0·80	0·90	0·79	0·81
1½	69	74	76	78	0·81	0·90	0·79	0·81
2	72	76	78	80	0·82	0·91	0·82	0·84
3	74	78	82	83	0·82	0·92	0·82	0·84
4	76	80	83	84	0·82	0·93	0·82	0·84
5	78	82	84	85	0·83	0·93	0·84	0·86
7½	81	83	85	86	0·84	0·94	0·85	0·87
10	81	84	87	88	0·84	0·94	0·86	0·88
12½	81	84	87	88	0·84	0·90	0·86	0·88
15	82	85	88	88	0·85	0·90	0·87	0·89
20	83	86	88	90	0·85	0·90	0·88	0·90
30	84	87	89	90	0·86	0·90	0·88	0·90
40	84	88	90	90	0·86	0·90	0·89	0·90
50	85	88	91	91	0·87	0·91	0·90	0·91
75	86	89	91	91	0·87	0·93	0·90	0·91
100	86	90	92	92	0·88	0·94	0·91	0·92

owever, starting characteristics similar to three-phase
quirrel-cage or slip-ring motors can be given by suitably
esigned capacitor motors.

Single-phase Series Motor.—A motor constructed some-
hat differently but connected in the same way as a d.c.
eries motor will run satisfactorily, and this type is sometimes
sed for single-phase traction work. The essential difference
a construction is that the field system must be laminated to
void iron losses with an alternating field and the stator
inding should be similar to that of an induction motor.

In performance it is similar to the d.c. series motor and the
peed decreases as the load increases. Unlike most a.c.
iotors, the power factor falls with the load and is highest on
ght loads.

Starting is usually arranged by means of an auto-trans-
ormer with variable tappings so that the motor is started on
reduced voltage which is increased to normal as the speed
ses.

In the *compensated series motor* an auxiliary field winding
s connected in series with the field between the armature and
he main field winding. This acts in the same way as the
iterpoles of a d.c. machine, neutralizing the cross-ampere
urns. Thus the low power factor on load is improved.

Repulsion Motors.—There are many forms of repulsion
iotors, but the main principle is that a stator winding similar
o a series motor is used with a wound rotor having a com-
iutator which is short-circuited. The brushes are set at an
ngle (about 70°) to the main field and by means of trans-
ormer action the field and armature fluxes are such that
hey repel each other and the rotor produces a torque.

Repulsion motors can be started either by a variable series
esistance or by auto-transformer, and a fair starting torque
an be obtained. On this account the principle is used for
tarting in the *repulsion-start single-phase induction motor*.
n this motor the rotor is as used for a repulsion motor, but
fter starting the two brushes are lifted and the commutator
hort-circuited all round by means of a copper ring. The
iotor then runs as an induction motor.

The speed of a repulsion motor driving a constant-torque
oad may be controlled either by movement of the brushes
r by variation of voltage applied to the motor. The former
nethod is usually adopted because of its simplicity and the
voidance of additional control gear.

SPEED VARIATION OF A.C. MOTORS

STANDARD types of a.c. motors do not permit of any real speed variation as their speeds are fixed by the frequency of the supply on which they operate. The synchronous motor has a definitely constant speed and the induction motor can be assumed as constant speed as the maximum slip is not usually more than 5 per cent. A limited speed variation can be obtained by rotor resistances.

Rotor Resistance Control.—The characteristic of the slip-ring machine with rotor resistance control approaches very closely to that of the series d.c. motor in that the speed rises as the load falls off and, therefore, it can only be satisfactorily employed for speed regulation where the load is fairly constant. Speed reduction by rotor resistance control is wasteful because of the power dissipated in the resistances resulting in a low overall efficiency. In general, accurate control of speed cannot be obtained with any degree of satisfaction below 30 to 40 per cent of full speed due to the fact that slight variation in the load causes wide fluctuations in the speed. In addition, difficulty may be experienced in maintaining constant speed due to the change of resistance with temperature of the external resistances, the speed tending to fall as the temperature of the controlling resistance increases.

With a suitable external resistance of the liquid type infinite variation between limits may be obtained, but with the metallic resistance grids and a drum controller, the number of steps of speed is, of course, limited to the number of settings in the controller, the resistances being graded to suit these steppings.

Pole-changing Motors.—As the speed of an induction motor depends on the number of poles, two, three or even four different speeds can be obtained by arranging the stator winding so that the number of poles may be changed. On a 50-cycle supply a pole-changing motor will give synchronous speeds of, say, 500, 1 000 and 1 500 r.p.m. No intermediate speeds can be obtained by this method. These motors are sometimes used for machine tools, as, for example, drilling machines, and this method gives a very convenient speed change.

Cascade Induction Motors.—Induction motors can be arranged in cascade form to give intermediate speeds. In this arrangement two motors are arranged so that the rotor of one motor is connected in series with the stator of the second, Fig. 22. Only one stator is fed from the supply.

The speed of the common shaft will be equal to that of a motor having a number of poles equal to the sum of those of the two motors. The speed of a cascade arrangement is thus a low value—usually an advantage for driving heavy machinery. For speed variation they can be arranged so that either the main motor can be used separately or in cascade. For instance, a combination of a 4-pole and 6-pole motor will give either 1,500 or 1,000 r.p.m. separately, or combined the speed will be

$$\frac{50 \times 60}{2 + 3} = 600 \text{ r.p.m.}$$

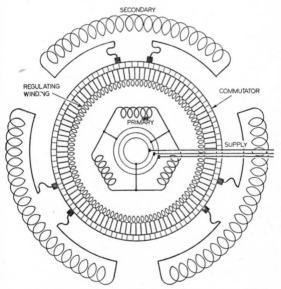

SECONDARY

REGULATING WINDING

COMMUTATOR

PRIMARY

SUPPLY

FIG. 23.—Diagram showing Windings of Three-phase Schrage Commutator Motor.

The Three-phase Commutator Motor (Schrage).—
The only fully variable speed motor for use on three-phase
is the commutator motor, one type of which is that due
to Schrage. The primary winding is situated on the rotor
and is fed by means of slip-rings. The rotor also carries a
secondary winding which is connected in the usual way to
the commutator and through the brushes to another secondary
winding on the stator.

Three pairs of brushes are required, each pair feeding one
phase of the stator winding, as shown in the diagram. Speed
variation is obtained by moving each pair of brushes relative
to each other, this being done by a hand or automatic control
through suitable worm-gear.

The speed range is roughly 3 to 1 for normal load—this
ranging from 40 per cent above to 60 per cent below synchronism. The speed varies from 5 to 20 per cent with the
load, but this can of course be counteracted by further movement of the brushes. Motors are usually started by placing
brushes in lowest speed position, giving a starting torque up
to $1\frac{1}{2}$ times full load torque.

These motors are expensive in first cost but have proved
very satisfactory for driving machinery requiring speed control, such as printing machines, textile mills, etc.

The higher initial cost over the slip-ring motor of corresponding rating is soon recovered because of the elimination
of rheostatic losses.

Motors for a speed range of 3 : 1 are available with ratings
from 3 h.p. to 250 h.p. Larger motors up to about 400 h.p.
can be built for a smaller speed range. Larger ranges of
speed up to 15 : 1 are possible, but they involve a more costly
motor, as the frame size for a given torque is governed by
the speed range.

Variable-speed Stator-fed Commutator Motor.—
Many applications requiring a variable-speed a.c. motor may
be met by the stator-fed commutator type.

This motor is similar to a slip-ring induction motor, with
the difference that the rotor winding is connected to a commutator instead of to slip-rings. Speed regulation is obtained
by means of a separate induction regulator connected between
the mains and the brushes on the commutator.

An auxiliary winding is often employed on the stator connected in series with the brushgear and the regulator, the
purpose being to increase the power factor of the motor
throughout its range of speeds.

The regulator acts as a variable-ratio transformer, supplying

STANDARDIZATION OF MOTOR DIMENSIONS

There are four parts to B.S. 2960 dealing with the standardization of motor dimensions. Part 1, issued in 1958, covers motors with ventilated enclosures; Part 2, issued in 1960, deals with totally-enclosed fan-cooled motors and this replaces B.S. 2083 : 1956; Parts 3 and 4, both published in 1964 deal with flameproof motors and slide rail dimensions respectively.

It is not practical to summarize the contents of all four parts in the Pocket Book, but the table given below shows the horsepower assignments for standard motor frames. In B.S. 2083 the dimensions relate to motors having windings insu-

HORSEPOWER ASSIGNMENTS FOR STANDARD MOTOR FRAMES

Nominal Output h.p.	Frame Sizes			
	Synchronous Speed at 50 c/s (Rev/Min).			
	3 000.	1 500.	1 000.	750.
$\frac{1}{2}$	—	—	D162	D164
$\frac{3}{4}$	—	—	D164	D182
1	—	D162	D182	D184
$1\frac{1}{2}$	D162	D164	D184	D213
2	D164	D182	D184	D213
3	D182	D184	D213	D215
5	D184	D213	D215	D254
$7\frac{1}{2}$	D213	D215	D254	D256
10	D215	D254	D256	D284
15	D254	D256	D286	D324
20	D256	D284	D324	D326
25	D284	D286	D326	D364
30	D286	D324	D364	D365
40	D324	D326	D365	D404
50	D326	D364	D404	D405
60	D365S*	D365	D405	—
75	D404S*	D404	—	—
100	D405S*	D405	—	—

* The letter S directly following the numerals indicates a motor with a small shaft extension for certain 2-pole machines where it is anticipated that the drive will be direct and not by means of a pulley.

lated with Class A material, whereas Parts 1, 2, and 3 of
B.S. 2960 are based on the use of Class E material which has
a higher permissible maximum temperature rise. In consequence, the horsepower outputs of motors now specified are
larger than those for comparable frame sizes in B.S. 2083.

The dimensions specified in the new Standard are, except
for the 162 and 164 frame sizes, similar to those specified in
the American N.E.M.A. Standard MG1–1955, but for a given
frame size the horsepower outputs have been increased in the
majority of cases to accord with the provisions of Class E
insulation. The shaft dimensions have been adjusted
accordingly.

While the British system of units is still retained in B.S.
2960 it should be borne in mind that the ultimate aim is to
embrace the metric system of measurement. Indeed, many
manufacturers already comply with the metric requirements.

The table below is extracted from B.S. 2960, Part 2 : 1960
and relates to totally-enclosed fan-cooled motors. The frame
size ranges for motors with ventilated enclosures and flame
proof motors do not always entirely correspond.

SYMBOLS FOR STANDARD DIMENSIONS
(FOOT-MOUNTED MOTORS)

Letter Symbol	Dimension Description	Letter Symbol	Dimension Description
A(max.)	Overall dimensions across feet of horizontal motor (end view)	F	Centre line of motor to centre line of mounting holes in feet (side view).
B(max.)	Overall dimensions across feet of horizontal motor (side view).	H	Diameter of holes or width of slot in feet of motor.
D(max.).	From centre line of shaft to bottom face of motor feet (nominal).	BA	From centre line of bolt holes, or slot, at driving end of motor to shoulder of shaft.
E	Centre line of motor to centre line of mounting holes in feet (end view).	U	Diameter of shaft exten- sion.
		V	Distance from shoulder of shaft to end of shaft (i.e. useful shaft extension).

MOTOR CONTROL GEAR

For safety, all motor starters should automatically return to the " off " position in the event of failure of the supply and for this purpose an undervoltage or " no-volt " release must be fitted. The undervoltage release forms an inherent part of the starting switch in all electro-magnetically-operated starters, but is additional to the starting-switch in hand-operated starters.

In faceplate d.c. starters the no-volt release takes the form of an electromagnet which holds the starter arm in the " full on " position by magnetic attraction (see Fig. 4, page 229).

With drum-type a.c. starters having a manually-operated starting handle, the starting switch is fitted with a spring which biases the switch to the " off " position, but is retained in the " on " position by a mechanical latch. Fitted in the starter is a shunt-wound electromagnet, or solenoid, excited by the supply voltage. In the event of supply failure, the plunger or armature of the solenoid or electromagnet is released, and is arranged to knock off the hold-on catch and so return the switch to the " off " position. A push-button for stopping the motor can be connected in series with the no-volt coil (see Fig. 1).

Contactor Control Gear.—In contactor starters, the no-volt feature is inherent as shown in Fig. 2. Pressing the starter button energizes the operating coil which closes the contactor. In order that the contactor may remain closed when the " start " push-button is released, retaining contacts are required. These are closed by the contactor lever itself and thus maintain the operating-coil circuit, once it has been made and the contactor closed, irrespective of the position of the " start " push-button. Depression of the " Stop " push-button, or failure of the supply to the operating coil, immediately causes the contactor to open. By energizing the operating coil from the same circuit as supplies the motor, such an arrangement is equivalent to a no-volt release.

When starting and stopping is automatically provided by means of a float, pressure or thermostatic switch, as in the case of motor-driven pumps, compressors, refrigerators and the like, two-wire control is used as in Fig. 3. In these cases, it is desirable that some form of hand reset device be incorporated with the overload release, to prevent the starter automatically reclosing after tripping on overload or fault until the reset button has been pressed after clearance of the fault.

MOTOR CONTROL GEAR

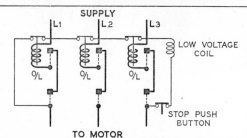

SUPPLY

L1   L2   L3

LOW VOLTAGE COIL

O/L   O/L   O/L

STOP PUSH BUTTON

TO MOTOR

FIG.1 DIAGRAM OF DRUM TYPE HAND OPERATED DIRECT -ON A.C. STARTER

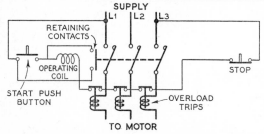

SUPPLY

L1   L2   L3

RETAINING CONTACTS

OPERATING COIL

STOP

START PUSH BUTTON

OVERLOAD TRIPS

TO MOTOR

FIG.2. DIAGRAM OF DIRECT-ON CONTACTOR STARTER

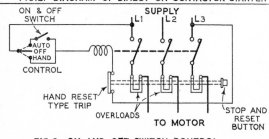

ON & OFF SWITCH

SUPPLY

L1   L2   L3

AUTO
OFF
HAND

CONTROL

HAND RESET TYPE TRIP

OVERLOADS   TO MOTOR

STOP AND RESET BUTTON

FIG.3. ON AND OFF SWITCH CONTROL

264

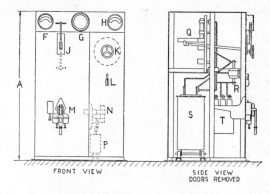

FRONT VIEW

SIDE VIEW
DOORS REMOVED

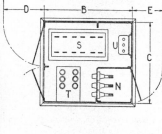

PLAN
ROOF AND CONNECTIONS REMOVED

SCHEMATIC CONNECTION DIAGRAM

F = Ammeter (stator).

G = Power factor meter.

H = Ammeter (field).

J = Operating handle of air-break change-over switch.

K = Operating handwheel for exciter field rheostat.

L = Field switch.

M = Operating handle for oil-circuit breaker with over-current trips and under-voltage release.

N = Isolators (if required).

P = Cable-box.

Q = Air-break change-over switch.

R = Current transformers.

S = Auto-transformer.

T = Oil circuit-breaker.

U = Cable rack.

Fig. 7.—Typical Auto-transformer Starting Panel.

(*A.E.I.*)

current. For squirrel-cage motors using either star-delta or transformer starting, the change-over from " start " to " run " is effected in contactor starters by employing two contactors with either a series or time relay for timing the moment of the change-over.

Wound-rotor Starters.—Where slip-ring motors have to start up against severe load conditions liquid resistance starters are found very satisfactory. By varying the electrolyte the added resistance is under control, and liquid starters have the advantage that the resistance is reduced continuously and smoothly instead of by steps as in other systems.

For wound-rotor motors hand-controlled starters are in more general use, but contactors can be used—one main contactor for the stator and two to five stages for cutting out the rotor resistance.

The change-over from one stage to another may be controlled by current or time. For current control a current or series relay is used to operate the change-over from one contactor to the next when the current has fallen to a certain value by virtue of the motor speeding up. This method ensures more correct starting but requires fairly accurate adjustment.

The time relay control is by means of a dash-pot time-lag or similar device, and as soon as the first contactor is operated the relay comes into circuit. After the set time has expired the change-over takes place and the process is repeated for subsequent stages.

Air-break Limits.—Manually-operated air-break switchgear and starters are only satisfactory up to a certain size. For d.c., however, air-break gear is used up to several hundred horse-power, but it is necessary to renew the contacts fairly frequently.

For controlling a.c. motors manually-operated air-break gear other than contactor gear is satisfactory up to about 30 h.p., but for larger outputs oil-break gear is generally specified. In this apparatus, where hand operation is required, contactors, hand-operated switches and rheostats may be oil immersed.

Fuses.—Overload devices in starters are designed to interrupt the circuit in the event of the current rising above a predetermined value due to the mechanical overloading of the motor, and are not usually designed to clear short-circuits. It is very desirable to include a circuit-breaker, or fuses, of sufficient breaking capacity to deal with any possible short

270

circuit that may occur. The required ratings of high-breaking capacity cartridge fuses for motor circuits can be obtained from fuse manufacturers' lists.

If rewirable fuses are used, they should blow at not more than four times full load motor current with a.c. direct switching and about twice with star-delta starting, in order to avoid overloading the heater coil or magnet coil burn-out on short-circuit before the fuse blows. Too low a fuse value may result in single-phasing troubles.

Quick-stopping of Motors.—The application of electric braking, that is, braking by causing the motor to develop a retarding torque, to certain classes of industrial drive, such as rolling mills, electric cranes and hoists, has been usual practice. There is no doubt, however, that braking by motor control for quick stopping could be applied with advantage and economy to common types of industrial drive where normally a friction brake is used, or no means of braking at all are provided. There are two possible fields of application : (1) drives where a large amount of energy is stored in the rotating parts of the driven machine ; and (2) drives requiring rapid and controlled deceleration in the event of an accident or emergency.

There are two ways in which a polyphase induction motor may be made to develop a braking torque and stop quickly : (1) by causing it to cease to act as a motor and to operate as a generator ; (2) by reversing it, so that it is, in effect, running backwards until its load is brought to rest. The first method is exemplified by the method of d.c. injection, and the second by " plugging."

Braking by D.C. Injection.—In this arrangement, when the motor is to be braked, it is disconnected from the a.c. supply and direct current is fed to the stator winding. The effect of this is to build up a static magnetic field in the space in which the rotor revolves and the current thereby generated in the rotor winding produces a powerful braking torque in exactly the same way as is done in a shunt-wound d.c. motor. In a workshop where a d.c. supply is available, the application of d.c. braking is particularly easy, as only little additional apparatus is required. In all other cases, the necessary d.c. can be provided by a rectifier built in or adjacent to the control box. No mechanical connections are required, all the braking control being included in the controller cabinet. When the stop button is pressed, the a.c. contactor (see Fig. 8) opens, causing the d.c. contactor to

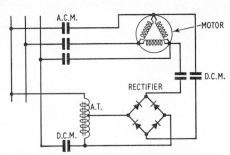

FIG. 8.—D.C. Injection.

A.T., auto-transformer; A.C.M., a.c. main contactor; D.C.M., d.c. main contactor.

(*Donovan Electrical Co., Ltd.*)

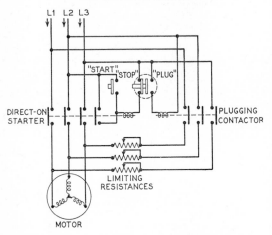

FIG. 9.—Wiring of Direct-on Contactor Starter for Plugging.

gas pressure sweeping the arc through vents in the side of the pot. Even at 150 MVA 11 kV most British Area Boards insist on some form of arc-control device.

All air circuit-breakers are fitted with arc chutes, the size of the chute depending on the voltage of the system. Only recently have air circuit-breakers been developed for use on 11 kV systems by British manufacturers, the previous limit being 3·3 kV 150 MVA. The main advantage of such units is the absence of oil, thus minimizing the fire risk. Maintenance is also simpler, but rating for rating the air circuit-breaker is more expensive. Arc extinction is effected by lengthening and cooling the arc until the voltage required to maintain it is greater than the system voltage.

For switchgear up to 150 MVA, or where the maximum short-circuit current does not exceed 22 kA at 3·3 kV or below, B.S. 116 allows the use of hand-closing mechanism. Above these ratings, power-closing devices are recommended ; these include solenoid, motor-operated, spring or hydraulic mechanisms. With the use of a solenoid it is usual to provide a low-voltage d.c. supply, whereas with motor control low-voltage three-phase a.c. can be employed. In most switchgear the action is by means of an over-centre toggle arrangement which ensures quick operation.

For ordinary distribution voltages three-phase units are used, but for the higher voltages used on the Grid scheme three separate single-phase breakers are often used in order to facilitate single-phase opening and closing for transient faults. Protection from overload is obtained by means of a releasing device which releases the mechanism and opens the switch. For small breakers the protection is obtained by means of overload coils or thermal releases inside the unit itself. For large units which are protected by some special system of protective gear the operation of one of the relays of the protective system releases the mechanism in a similar manner.

Some essential features of oil-break switchgear are :

(a) Isolation of internal mechanism for inspection. This is important and full interlocks are always provided to prevent opening of any part of the enclosure unless every part of the breaker is disconnected from the supply.

(b) Quantity of oil and clearance from breaker contacts to sides of tank must be adequate for voltage and maximum load which the breaker will be called upon to deal with.

(c) Provision for manual operation in case the electrical control (if provided) fails to operate.

(d) Provision for any instruments which may be required. These may be in the form of either ammeter or voltmeter on the unit itself or the necessary current and potential transformers for connecting to the main switchboard or separate instrument panel.

For high voltage work oil-break switchgear is isolated in the following ways :

(a) By isolating links in or near the busbar chamber.

(b) Draw-out type of gear in which the whole of the circuit-breaker is withdrawn vertically from the busbar chamber before it can be opened up.

(c) Truck-type, in which the circuit-breaker with its connections is isolated in a horizontal manner before inspection or adjustment.

It should be noted that in certain cases, double isolating devices are necessary, i.e. both on the incoming and outgoing side. Isolation is, of course, always required on the incoming side, but it is also necessary on the outgoing side if that part of the network can be made alive through any other control gear or alternative supply. With conventional switchgear isolation of both sides takes place automatically.

It is interesting to note that one explanation of the difference between a switch and circuit-breaker is that whereas the switch is a device for making and breaking a current not greatly in excess of its rated normal current, the circuit-breaker is a device capable of making and breaking the circuit under both normal and abnormal conditions. Oil switches, however, have to be capable of making onto a short-circuit at a very low power factor.

There is to-day a large amount of research work still being carried on both in the laboratory and by interchange of views between manufacturers all over the world.

A breaker is usually classified according to the voltage of the circuit on which it is to be installed ; the normal current which it is designed to carry continuously in order to limit the temperature rise to a safe value ; the frequency of the supply ; its interrupting capacity in MVA ; its making capacity in amperes, i.e. the instantaneous peak current ; and the greatest r.m.s. current which it will carry without damage for a specified length of time, usually 1 or 3 seconds.

A number of oil circuit-beaker MVA breaking capacities have been standardized for use in this country. These capacities are given in the table which is reproduced from the B.S. 116.

STANDARD THREE-PHASE OIL CIRCUIT-BREAKERS
Preferred ratings
(excluding pole-mounting and flameproof circuit-breakers)

Service Voltage kV.	Breaking Capacity MVA.	Symmetrical Breaking kA.	Normal Currents A.				
			400	600	800	1 200	1 600
0·415	26	36		600	800	1 200	1 600
3·3	50	8·76	400				
	75	13·1	400		800		
	150	26·3			800	1 200	
6·6	150	13·1	400		800		
	250	21·9			800	1 200	
11	150	7·88	400		800		
	250	13·1	400		800		
	500	26·3			800	1 200	
33	500	8·76	400		800		
	750	13·1	400		800	1 200	
	1 500	26·3			800	1 200	
66	1 500	13·1			800		
	2 500	21·9			800	1 200	
132	2 500	10·9		600			
	3 500	15·3			800		

Flameproof circuit-breakers

Service Voltage kV.	Breaking Capacity MVA.	Symmetrical Breaking kA.	Normal Currents A.		
			400	600	800
0·415	5·2	7·25		250	400
0·6	3·75	3·6	150		
3·3	25·0	4·38	150	250	

Note: (1) No doubt a future revision of B.S. 116 will include 275 kV circuit-breakers as preferred ratings. At present the standard ratings are 3 500, 5 000, and 7 500 MVA.

(2) Air circuit-breakers tend to follow similar ratings where applicable.

OVERLOAD AND FAULT PROTECTION

PROTECTION against electrical faults may be broadly divided into fusegear or circuit-breakers. In some instances fuses are fitted into circuit-breakers but this practice is dying out. Another similar arrangement is that of fuses fitted in series with an oil switch and so arranged that upon the blowing of a fuse-link a striker pin is ejected and arranged to trip the oil switch.

Types of Fuses.—The simplest and cheapest forms of protection against excess current is the fuse. Two types of fuse are in use:

(1) The semi-enclosed type, comprising removable porcelain holder with handle through which the fuse-wire passes.

(2) The totally enclosed or cartridge type fuse in which the fuse itself is enclosed by a cylinder of hard, non-combustible material having metal capped ends, which is filled with non-flammable powder, or other special material.

The wires used in semi-enclosed fuses are usually either tinned copper or lead-tin alloy, though other metals such as aluminium or lead may sometimes be used. The table on page 283 shows fuse wire sizes and fusing currents for the different types of fuse wire likely to be met with in practice.

For the sake of completeness mention should be made of two types of fuses used on rural systems, namely expulsion and liquid.

The Rating of Fuses.—The selection of fuses is a difficult problem, the rating depending on the circuit the fuse is protecting. For circuits controlling non-inductive loads such as lighting, the fuse rating can be safely based on the full load of the circuit being protected. Thus if the full load is 14·8 amperes a 15-ampere fuse would be satisfactory. On the other hand if the fuse is controlling an inductive or capacitive circuit the fuse rating is based upon the maximum inrush current and its duration at the instant of switching on. This, in most cases, works out that the fuse rating is between two and three times the full load current of the circuit. Standard fuse ratings must of course be chosen and thus the next highest rating above the " worked out " current must be selected.

H.B.C. Cartridge-type fuses. *—Cartridge-type fuses are available for systems up to 660 V in current ratings from 2 to 800 amperes and breaking capacity ratings increases to 35 MVA. Above 400-ampere current ratings, heat dissipation is difficult and the tendency is to limit the upper current ratings to this figure. Higher MVA ratings can be obtained but they are not standard. Fig. 1 shows the cross-section of a m.v. fuse.

For h.v. systems from up to 11 kV the breaking capacity ratings rise to 250 MVA three-phase and current ratings are usually around the 200-ampere mark.

Other advantages of correctly-designed high-breaking capacity fuses are:

Discrimination.—The fuse nearest the fault will operate, thus ensuring that only the faulty circuit is isolated and healthy circuits are unaffected. This discriminating property is inherent in cartridge-type fuses, as a glance at the current-fusing time curves for different sizes of fuse in Fig. 2 will show. It will be seen that the speed of operation for any particular value of overload or fault current increases as the fuse gets smaller. This is bound up with another property of h.b.c. fuses—non-deterioration.

High Speed of Operation on Short-circuit.—This property enables h.r.c. fuses to be used for the back-up protection of motor starters and low break-ing capacity circuit-breakers, although as mentioned above this practice is rapidly vanishing. For such purposes high breaking capacity in itself is not sufficient. The speed of operation of the fuses used for back-up protection must be faster than the speed of operation of the motor starter or circuit breaker to be protected; otherwise the apparatus under protection would be damaged or destroyed before the fuses had time to act.

---

* The British Standard recommends the term " high breaking capacity " (h.b.c.) and not " high rupturing capacity " (h.r.c.).

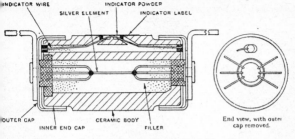

INDICATOR WIRE   INDICATOR POWDER
SILVER ELEMENT   INDICATOR LABEL

OUTER CAP
INNER END CAP   CERAMIC BODY   FILLER

End view, with outer cap removed.

Fig. 1.—Construction of H.B.C. Cartridge Fuse.
(G.E.C.)

Selection of Fuses.—When selecting suitable fuses for any particular situation the following factors should be considered :—

(1) *The breaking capacity of the fuse* should be sufficient to clear the estimated short-circuit current in the conductor. If fuses of inadequate breaking capacity are used, and they are called upon to clear a short-circuit in excess of the value with which they can safely deal, the fuses and metal-clad enclosures may be completely destroyed.

(2) *The current rating of the fuse.*—This is the maximum current which the fuse will carry continuously without deterioration. The current rating of the fuse should not be more than the normal full load current rating of the conductor in which the fuse is to be used. An exception to this is the case of motor circuits which are dealt with in paragraph (4). Suitable sizes of tinned copper wire for rewirable fuses are given on page 283. H.B.C. cartridge fuses are marked.

(3) *The Minimum Fusing Current of the Fuse.* —This is defined as the minimum r.m.s. current at which a fuse-element in a fuse will melt. Commercial fuses, wired with tinned copper fuse wire, will blow at currents 170 per cent normal up to 60 amps., and 200 per cent for the larger sizes, whilst cartridge fuses are usually

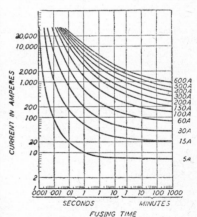

Fig. 2.—Current Fusing Time Curves for Typical Cartridge Fuses.

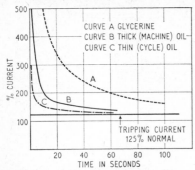

CURVE A GLYCERINE
CURVE B THICK (MACHINE) OIL
CURVE C THIN (CYCLE) OIL

TRIPPING CURRENT
125% NORMAL

Fig. 3.—Characteristic for Series Trip Coil with Oil Dashpot.

arranged to blow at lower percentages of normal current, e.g. 160 per cent. It is possible to obtain h.b.c. fuses that will blow with accuracy at currents as low as 120 per cent normal.

Another way of conveying this property of a fuse is referred to as the fusing factor—this is the minimum fusing current divided by the current rating, thus 170 per cent normal current corresponds to a fusing factor of 1·7.

(4) *When fusing for motor circuits*, the rating of the fuse selected should be such that all overloads (as distinct from electrical faults) within the capacity of the starter should be dealt with by the starter. It is obviously undesirable that the fuses should operate on overloads when a motor starter is available for this purpose. When the thermal or magnetic overload device in the starter deals with an overload, the operator can restart the motor after having removed the cause of the overload. If, however, the fuse is also arranged to operate on similar overloads, then not only would the fuse have to be replaced but unnecessary delay in restarting the motor would occur.

In selecting the current rating of fuses for a given motor circuit, it is necessary to take into account the starting current, which may be considerably in excess of the normal full load current of the motor, depending on the type of motor and method of starting.

When selecting h.b.c. fuses for motor circuits, the required ratings can be obtained from the tables published by the fuse manufacturer. If, owing to special conditions, there is any doubt, the question should be referred to the makers of the fuse concerned.

The fuse rating chosen for the protection of induction motor circuits is about 3 to 3½ times the normal current of the circuit. This may have to be varied to suit unusual conditions, such as a very long starting period or very frequent starting, but in ordinary circumstances is accepted as the usual value.

The Automatic Circuit-breaker.—Circuit-breaker equipment, whilst considerably more expensive than fuse gear protection, possesses important features which render it essential on all circuits where accurate and repetitive operation is required. It is usually employed on all main circuits fusegear being reserved for sub-circuits.

Overload Releases.—The simplest automatic release used is the direct acting over-current coil, which is a solenoid energized by the current passing through the unit, and calibrated to operate when this reaches a predetermined value. The trip setting is adjustable, from normal full load current up to 300 per cent for instantaneous release and 200 per cent for time lag release. Therefore a setting as near as is desired to full load current can be obtained. On a three-phase insulated system, coils in two phases will give full protection, since any fault must involve two phases : but with an earthed system, release coils must be provided in all three phases, unless

282

leakage protection is also provided, when two overcurrent coils will again suffice. In small current sizes it is usual to make the over-current coils direct series connected : but in larger sizes the coils are often operated from current transformers.

Time Lags.—If full advantage is to be taken of the facility to obtain close overcurrent settings that is offered by circuit-breakers, some form of restraining device is necessary to retard the action of the releases, as this is normally instantaneous. This retarding device, or time lag, usually takes the form of a piston and dash-pot. Its purpose is to delay the action of the trips so as to allow for sudden fluctuations in the load, and also to give a measure of discrimination. In practice, a characteristic closely resembling that of a fuse is obtained, and a typical characteristic for an oil dash-pot time lag—perhaps the most common type in general use—is given in Fig. 3.

Use of Time-limit Fuses.—When the overcurrent coils are transformer operated, it is possible to use a shunt fuse in place of the mechanical retarder. These fuses are designed to short-circuit the trip coils, which, therefore, cannot operate until the fuse has blown. The fuse itself is usually of allo-tin wire or some other non-deteriorating metal, and is accurately calibrated as regards blowing current. When time-limit fuses are used, no advantage is to be gained by making the release coils themselves adjustable : and alternative trip settings are obtained by varying the blowing current of the fuses.

H.B.C. Fuses and Circuit-breakers.—With a circuit-breaker, a certain time must elapse between the operation of the tripping mechanism and the actual breaking of the current, and with commercial types of breaker this time is usually of the order of 0·1 sec. On the other hand, a high breaking capacity fuse is capable of clearing a very heavy fault in less than half a cycle ; and, therefore, it will operate in these conditions long before a breaker has had time even to start the opening operation.

CARRYING CAPACITY OF FUSES

Carrying Capacity in Amperes.	Fuse Wire Sizes (S.W.G.) based on fusing at twice the Normal Full Load Current.				
	Copper.	Lead-Tin.	Aluminium.	Iron.	Lead.
5	34	21	33	24	20
10	30	17	29	20	17
15	28	14	27	18	14
20	26	13	23	17	13
25	24	11	22	16	11
30	22	10	2/27	15	10
35	21	9	—	14	9
40	20	8	2/23	13	8
50	19	7	2/22	12	7
60	18	—	—	—	—
70	17	—	—	—	—
80	16	—	—	—	—
90	—	—	—	—	—
100	15	—	—	—	—

RELAYS AND PROTECTIVE GEAR

THE protection of both plant and transmission lines has reached a very high state of perfection and faulty sections can now be automatically isolated before a fault or overload can cause any damage to the section itself or the remainder of the system of which it is a part.

In all the different methods the essential feature is that of isolating the faulty section, and in considering the principles of the various systems of protection it is usually understood that the actual isolation is carried out by circuit-breakers which, in turn, are operated by means of currents due to the action of the protective gear. Usually the required operating current for the breaker is controlled by relays which are in turn operated by the protective gear.

Similar principles are used for the protection of machines such as alternators, transformers, etc., as for overhead lines and cables. The essential difference is only a matter of adaptation, the most important difference being the fact that on transmission lines and feeders certain systems require pilot wires connecting the protective apparatus at each end of the line and these are sometimes undesirable. With machines this point is unimportant as the two sets of gear — one on each side — are not separated by any real distance.

With all systems one or both of the following two undesirable features are guarded against—namely, *overload* and *faulty insulation*. The overload conditions which make it necessary to disconnect the supply may be due to faulty apparatus or to an overload caused by connecting apparatus of too great a capacity for the line or machine. The faulty insulation or *fault* conditions may be either between the conductors or from one or all the conductors to earth.

In connection with all protective gear the following terms are generally used :

Stability Ratio.—This may be termed the measure of the discriminating power of the system. The stability is referred to as the maximum current which can flow without affecting the proper functioning of the protective gear. Stability ratio can also be defined as the ratio between stability and the sensitivity.

Sensitivity is the current (in primary amperes), which will operate the protective gear. In the case of feeders and transmission lines this is a measure of the difference between the current entering the line and the current leaving it.

OVERCURRENT RELAYS

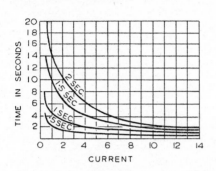

FIG.1 INVERSE TIME-LAG CHARACTERISTICS
OF OVERCURRENT RELAYS

FIG.2 GRADING OF OVERCURRENT RELAYS

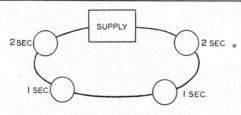

FIG 3 GRADING FOR RING MAINS.

OVERLOAD RELAYS

The simplest form of protection is that where the circuit breaker is opened as soon as the current exceeds a predetermined value. For d.c. circuits of small capacity simple overload breakers are usually mounted on the switchboard over the rest of the switchgear. For high-voltage a.c. systems, oil or air or air blast circuit-breakers must be used and the trip coils of these breakers are operated by overcurrent relays with graded time-lag characteristics.

The time-current characteristics will be seen from the curves in Fig. 1, which show how the time lag before the overload occurring and the gear operating is inversely proportional to the amount of the overload. The setting or time lag usually used to indicate how the relay has been adjusted is that of short-circuit conditions so that the settings of the four relays for which the curves are drawn would be as marked.

The principle of grading on a system is that of decreasing the setting as we proceed away from the source of supply. The use of the four relays for which the curves have been drawn would be as shown in the diagrams in Figs. 2 and 3. Fig. 2 represents a distributor fed at one end, whereas Fig. 3 shows a ring main. A distributor fed at both ends is similar to Fig. 3.

Modern overcurrent relays are usually of the induction type. The action is similar to that of an induction watt-meter. A metal disc rotates against a spring, the angle of rotation being proportional to the current. As soon as the disc has rotated through a certain angle the trip circuit is closed. As the speed of rotation is proportional to the load the inverse time element is obtained and the time-setting is adjustable by altering the angle through which the disc has to turn before making the trip circuit.

DIRECTIONAL PROTECTION

In addition to overload protection it is often desirable for immediate interruption of supply in the case of a reverse current. In this case directional relays are used and these can be combined with overcurrent relays when required as shown in Fig. 4. The use of directional and non-directional relays is shown in the system reproduced in Fig. 6.

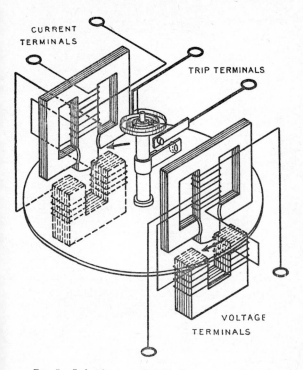

CURRENT
TERMINALS

TRIP TERMINALS

VOLTAGE
TERMINALS

Fig. 5.—Induction-type Definite Impedance Relay.

protecting transmission lines and balanced current for
protecting machines.

The balanced voltage system was developed for line protection and is illustrated in Fig. 9. This is known as the
Merz-Price System. There have been several modifications
and most manufacturers have their own particular method of
applying this principle and improving the actual performance
compared with the original simple Merz-Price System.

A typical modification is the Translay System in which

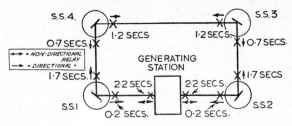

Fig. 6.—Discriminative Time Protection of Ring Main.

Fig. 7.—Balanced Voltage System.

Fig. 8.—Balanced Current System.

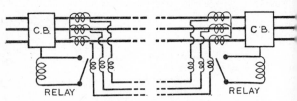

Fig. 9.—Three-phase Merz-Price System.

induction type relays are used instead of the usual electro-magnetic type. The circuit (simplified) is given in Fig. 10. The relay primary winding is energized from the secondary of a current transformer and in addition to setting up a

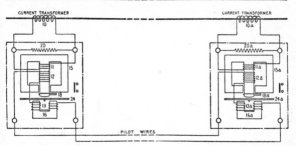

FIG. 10.—The Translay System for Single-phase Feeder.

leakage flux which, in conjunction with a suitable flux from the lower magnet, causes the non-magnetic disc to rotate, it acts also as the primary of an air-gap transformer causing a voltage to be generated in the secondary winding. The value of this secondary voltage depends on the current flowing in the primary winding, and as the secondary windings of the relays at opposite ends of the feeder are connected in opposition through the pilot wires, no current will flow in the circuit under normal conditions. In the case of a fault, there is a discrepancy between the currents flowing at the two ends, and the resultant difference between the secondary voltages will cause a current to flow in this circuit. The flux set up by this current will, by interaction with the leakage flux, cause the relays to operate.

This system, which has been developed by Messrs. Metro-politan-Vickers Electrical Co., Ltd., now part of the Associated Electrical Industries Ltd., removes many of the disadvantages.

A differential reverse scheme is shown in Fig. 13, for additional protection of a generator against reverse current due to breakdown between turns of the same phase, failure of excitation, or prime-mover trouble. The diagram shows the voltage transformer required, and the current biassing value given to the current transformer at the switchboard end under normal conditions of full load.

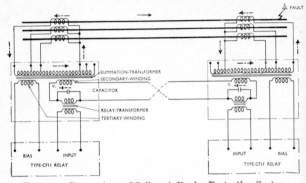

FIG. 11.—Connections of Solkor-A Feeder Protective System
(*A. Reyrolle & Co. Ltd.*)

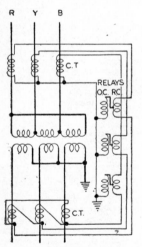

FIG. 12.—Transformer Protection. (Star-delta connection)

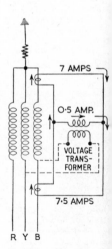

FIG. 13.—Alternator Protection.

Owing to the quick heating of small quantities of water the circulator is very suitable for hand control. Circulators are available for both top and bottom entry.

Necessary Pipe Alterations.—As mentioned previously, the most important point in designing an immersion heater or circulator installation is to make certain that the existing hot-water installation is suitable for conversion. The chief difference between a system heated by a coal- or coke-fired boiler and that heated by means of an immersion heater is the position of the source of heat. The boiler is normally situated below the hot-water tank and the heated water is fed into the tank through the flow-pipe. An immersion heater is actually fitted in the tank where the hottest water will always be at the top. It is important, therefore, that the hot-water taps should be fed from the top of the tank. In Fig. 1 some of the faults commonly found in hot-water installations are shown. There are three primary faults shown, which must be removed if satisfactory results are to be obtained. The kitchen tap is fed from the boiler flow-pipe and consequently will not, when the electric heater is in use, give a supply of water at the full possible temperature. In fact, the water may be practically cold. It is obvious that water would be drawn from both the boiler and the tank, but as the water in the boiler is cold the water actually drawn at the tap would be a mixture of hot water from the tank and cold water from the boiler. Sometimes all the taps in an installation are fed from the boiler flow-pipe and it is then necessary to alter them so that they are fed from the top of the tank. The alteration to the piping to the kitchen tap is shown by a dotted line in Fig. 1. The original pipe must be disconnected from the boiler flow pipe.

It will be noticed that the expansion pipe B is taken some little way into the hot-water tank. Not only does this mean that water is drawn from a position too low in the tank but it is possible for an air-lock to occur at the top of the tank which may result in damage to the heater. The expansion pipe should finish flush with the top of the tank.

Another possible source of trouble is the cold-water inlet A which has not been taken low enough into the tank. When the cold water enters the hot tank through this short pipe it causes considerable mixing with the contained hot water, with the result that the full contents of the tank will not be available at the highest possible temperature. Sometimes,

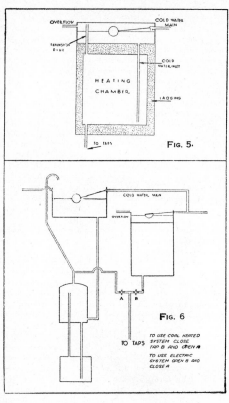

OVERFLOW COLD WATER MAIN
EXPANSION PIPE
COLD WATER INLET
HEATING CHAMBER
LAGGING
TO TAPS
FIG. 5.

COLD WATER MAIN
OVERFLOW
A B
FIG. 6
TO TAPS
TO USE COAL HEATED
SYSTEM CLOSE
TAP B AND OPEN A
TO USE ELECTRIC
SYSTEM OPEN B AND
CLOSE A

Note to Fig. 6.—If taps A and B are both left open, the cistern heater
tank will become flooded via its expansion pipe.

298

when a circulator has been fitted to a tank, trouble will be experienced by the premature cutting out of the thermostat. Very often this is due to the tank not standing level, with the result that an air-lock occurs at the top on the opposite side to the point where the expansion pipe is connected. Generally speaking, a circulator would be fitted on this side owing to the larger space available and, if the air-lock is sufficiently great, the hot-water outlet ports (or holes) on the circulating tube will be above the water-level. This effectively prevents circulation, so that the thermostat cuts out when the water in the circulating tube has reached the set temperature.

There are a large number of hot-water installations in which a secondary circulation is employed in order to reduce the amount of dead water that would otherwise have to be drawn off before hot water was available. In Fig. 2 a typical lay-out of such an installation is shown. It will be seen that the whole time there is a difference in temperature between the points A and B there will be a circulation from the tank along the pipe C and back to the tank through the pipe D. The loss of heat from such a pipe as this situated in the roof, as it usually is, might under average conditions be 1·5 B.t.u. per degree difference in temperature per square foot of pipe surface ; thus 30 feet of 1-inch pipe (and both flow and return must be taken into consideration), having a surface of 10·4 square feet, would lose almost 500 watts per hour with a water temperature of 160° F.

The loss of heat from any object depends on the nature of its surface and the number of changes of the air surrounding it. Apart from the question of difference of temperature it is, therefore, impossible to lay down hard-and-fast rules for the calculation of the loss of heat. A galvanized-iron hot-water tank situated in a linen cupboard with the door closed loses approximately 1 B.t.u. per square foot of surface per degree F. difference in temperature. This result was obtained from a number of actual tests carried out under working conditions. A rough formula for the calculation is, therefore, as follows :

Loss of heat in kilowatt-hours

$$= \frac{\text{square feet of surface} \times \text{temperature difference degrees F.}}{3412}$$

It must be used with great caution, for in some situations it is possible that the actual loss may be double the calculated figure. If a tank is " lagged " the formula may be adjusted to include the heat-insulating properties of the "lagging" material.

Loss of heat in kilowatt-hours

$$= \frac{\dfrac{K}{t} \times \text{square feet} \times \text{temperature difference degrees F.}}{3412}$$

where K is the conductivity of the "lagging" material and t is the thickness in inches. The figure for K should be obtained from the manufacturers of the insulating material, but, in any case, it should be doubled to allow a margin of safety.

The formula for calculating the time taken to heat a given quantity of water through a given temperature rise with a given loading is:

$$\text{Time} = \frac{\text{gallons} \times \text{temperature rise degrees F.}}{341 \times \text{percentage efficiency} \times \text{kilowatts}}$$

The calculation of any other unknown quantity may be made by adjusting the above formula. For reference purposes the various formulæ are set down below.

Kilowatts required to raise temperature of water through given temperature rise:

$$\frac{\text{gallons} \times \text{temperature rise degrees F.}}{341 \times \text{percentage efficiency}}$$

Kilowatts required to raise given quantity of water through given temperature rise in a given time:

$$\frac{\text{gallons} \times \text{temperature rise degrees F.}}{341 \times \text{time in hours} \times \text{percentage efficiency}}$$

Temperature rise per hour with a given loading acting on a given quantity of water:

$$\frac{\text{kilowatts} \times 341 \times \text{percentage efficiency}}{\text{gallons}}$$

Temperature rise after a given time for a given loading acting on a given quantity of water:

$$\frac{\text{kilowatts} \times 341 \times \text{time in hours} \times \text{percentage efficiency}}{\text{gallons}}$$

Gallons per hour raised through given temperature rise with given loading:

$$\frac{341 \times \text{kilowatts} \times \text{percentage efficiency.}}{\text{temperature rise degrees F.}}$$

If an efficiency of 88 per cent is assumed it is possible to simplify some of the above formulæ. This figure substituted in the first formula gives

Time in hours

$$= \frac{\text{gallons} \times \text{temperature rise degrees F.}}{\text{kilowatts} \times 300} \quad \text{approx.}$$

which is very easily remembered.

Useful Temperatures and Calculations

Cold water	40° to 50° F.
Comfortable room temperature .	60° to 70° F.
Bath water	105° to 110° F.
Dish washing	120° to 140° F.
Scalding water	150° F.
Boiling water	212° F.

The calculations necessary in order to obtain the capacity of a tank or cylinder are as follows :

Rectangular Tank :

$$\text{Gallons} = \frac{\text{height} \times \text{width} \times \text{depth}}{276}.$$

Cylindrical Tank :

$$\text{Gallons} = \frac{\text{diameter} \times \text{diameter} \times 0 \cdot 78 \times \text{depth}}{276}.$$

All the above measurements are in inches.

Self-contained Storage Heaters.—There are four distinct types of self-contained storage heaters in general use and each is designed to meet certain conditions.

The Non-Pressure type heater is designed to supply hot water to one position only through a permanently open outlet, the control of the flow of water being achieved by means of a tap or stopcock inserted in the inlet pipe. This type of heater may be connected direct to the water main, subject of course to the water company's restrictions as to maximum capacity. The 1½- and 3-gallon storage heaters are very suitable for fitting over the kitchen sink. Even when an immersion heater is fitted it is sometimes an economy to use a self-contained unit to supply points which are some distance from the hot-water tank. Fig. 3 shows the water connections to a non-pressure type storage heater.

The Pressure type heater is suitable for connection direct to a low-pressure cold-water supply such as would be available from the ordinary domestic cold-water cistern. It may be arranged to supply any number of taps compatible with its capacity. Another use for the pressure type heater is to provide an alternative supply of hot water to that provided by the coal- or coke-fired boiler. Such an arrangement is shown in Fig. 4.

The Cistern type heater, as its name implies, has a small cold-water cistern fitted above the heating chamber. It is really a complete hot-water system in one outer case. The cistern type heater may be connected direct to the cold-water main and it can be arranged to supply any number of taps. It must, of course, be fitted at a position above the highest tap it is to feed. As an alternative supply it may be interconnected into the existing hot-water system. Figs. 5 and 6 show cistern type heaters arranged as described above.

The "Two-in-One" Heater is a pressure heater provided with two thermostatically-controlled heating elements fitted horizontally at two levels inside its cylinder. The top heating element (usually loaded to 500 watts) is situated about a quarter of the way down, in which position it heats about a quarter of the contents only. The lower element (2,500 watts) at the bottom of the cylinder heats the remainder. The inlet is at the side of the heater, while the outlet is taken from the top of the cylinder through the lagging to the side of the casing, from where it is connected to the taps it has to supply.

In normal use both elements are working under the control of their separate thermostats, but when the demand is likely to be slack for more than, say, 24 hours, the bottom element can be switched off independently, thereby reducing the amount of hot water in storage. The upper element alone will provide an ample supply of hot water for sink and wash-basin use, because although there is cold water at the bottom of the cylinder the hotter water will float above it. The two-in-one heater is, therefore, a more flexible appliance than the ordinary water heater and with its higher loading has a quicker recovery when both elements are switched on.

The consumption of electric water heaters depends to a large extent on the quantity of hot water used. For purposes of comparison some average figures are given below.

Immersion heaters or circulators	40 to 70	units per week
1½- and 3-gallon storage heaters	15 to 30	,, ,, ,,
12-gallon storage heaters . .	4 to 5	units per bath
20-gallon storage heaters . .	50 to 80	units per week

SPACE HEATING

HEATING appliances for domestic use are of the fixed or portable type, the latter being connected by socket-outlets, plugs and flexible cords. For industrial use space heating takes the form of underfloor heating, thermal storage, or infra-red heating. The main types of heating appliances for domestic use are :

Radiant Heaters.—(1) Reflector fires, where the heat is controlled and projected by a parabolic reflector ; (2) flat-bar fires, which emit a gentle radiant heat. Both these types may be either inset designs (made to be built into the wall) or ordinary portables. Standard ratings are from 0·75 kW to 3 kW.

Convector Heaters.—(1) The conventional convector, the heat from which emanates from an element that does not attain a red heat (this type of heater may be either fixed or portable) ; (2) hot water or oil convector or " radiator " electrically-heated (fixed) ; (3) tubular heater (fixed).

Panel and Flood Heaters.—Available in low-, medium and high-temperature types.

Fan Heaters.—An electric element with a fan mounted so as to blow warm air into the room.

Underfloor Heating.—This form of heating in which electric cables are embedded in the floor of a building and arranged to heat it is about 5 years old. It takes one of two forms : the first is where the cable is embedded direct in the concrete and is thus non-withdrawable ; the second is where the cable is drawn into conduit which is embedded in the concrete— this type is withdrawable.

Ceiling Heating.—A new system under development and basically similar to floor warming. The heating elements are cast into the lower part of the concrete floor slab to heat the room below.

Thermal Storage Heating.—Heating elements are embedded in a solid concrete block contained in a sheet metal casing approximately the same shape as a normal convector heater. This system is also known as unit-plan heating.

Infra-red Heaters.—These make use of the heating effect of the 3 micron emanations from black-heat elements.

Radiant Heaters.—There are already available on the market reflector type fires having a high degree of radiant efficiency. These fires have highly polished parabolic reflectors so arranged that an average room is flooded with radiant heat. In some fires side reflectors are fitted which add greatly to their effect. With a correctly designed reflector type fire it is possible to heat a room 11 feet 6 inches by 13 feet 6 inches by 8 feet with a maximum loading of 1,250 watts. If the loading required to heat such a room is calculated by one of the usual formulae the loading apparently required is considerably higher. Thus :

$$1{,}242 \times 0{\cdot}02 \times 2 \times 30 = 1{,}490{\cdot}4 \text{ B.t.u.}$$

while the loss of heat in the example taken is :—

60 square feet glass windows	1,854	B.t.u.
32 square feet outside wall	316	,,
155 square feet ceiling	395	,,
155 square feet floor	8	,,
200 square feet inside walls	880	,,
108 square feet 9-inch inside wall	534	,,

giving a total of 3,987 B.t.u. loss of heat per hour. The calculated loading is, therefore, nearly 2 kW. This figure would be correct if ordinary heaters were used which give off a large proportion of their heat by air convection currents. It will be seen that if a room of average size can be effectively heated with a maximum loading of 1,250 watts during the very cold weather, and a loading of, say, 750 watts during the warmer weather, the average consumption throughout the period heating is required is approximately one unit per hour. With current at 1·7d. per unit the cost per day would be about 1s. 8d., a figure which compares very favourably with coal heating if the standing charge is ignored.

Recent developments in direct-acting heating systems include some new types of ceiling heating. These emit low-temperature radiation from special prefabricated heating mats which are designed for ceiling mounting ; they are intended for continuous operation under thermostatic control and have been widely used in Scandinavian countries. These systems have particular application in buildings with a high degree of thermal insulation incorporating a low thermal capacity lining to the exterior walls. As efficient thermal insulation of the building becomes more general, direct-acting heating systems may well become more widely used.

Convector Heaters.—Reflector type fires are not generally so suitable for heating halls, landings or passages. In these situations convector or air heating is very effective. The air heaters are best thermostatically controlled at a temperature between 50° and 60° F. according to individual tastes. Higher temperatures than 60° F. are quite unnecessary and tend to make a house stuffy. It is excessive air temperatures which give rise to this complaint often made about central heating. A good average temperature for a hall or landing is 55° F. When air heating is being considered it is necessary to know the approximate loss of heat likely to take place through walls, etc. The following coefficients give the loss in B.t.u. per square foot of surface per degree F. per hour :—

9-inch plastered wall	0·33
4½-inch plastered wall	0·44
Lath and plaster ceiling with wood floor above (cold air above)	0·17
Ditto (with cold air below)	0·07
Wood floor with air space and concrete foundations	0·05
Tiled boarded roof	0·35
Tiled roof and lath and plaster ceiling . .	0·24
Single glass windows	1·03

The amount of heat required to raise the temperature of one cubic foot of air one degree F. is approximately 0·02 B.t.u. A point to be remembered in calculating the loss of heat through a wall is the difference in temperature which will differ for each wall. For example, the difference in temperature between the inside and outside of an outside wall would probably be 30° F. in very cold weather, while the difference in temperature between the faces of an inside wall might only be a matter of 10° F., depending on the amount of heating in the other room or passage. In the case of bedrooms, the difference in temperature between a living-room below and the bedroom may be about 15° F.

When calculating the heat required to raise the temperature of the air in a room it must be remembered that ventilation is continually going on and therefore the quantity of air to be heated is considerably more than the cubical contents of the room. It is usual to take two air changes per hour for a living-room and three air changes per hour for a hall. Where a room has a north aspect or is situated in a very windy position it is usual to add 10 per cent. to the calculated loss.

A good example of a convector heater is the tubular heater which can be fitted along the skirting-board. Even in a room heated by radiant heaters it is sometimes an advantage to make up for any undue loss of heat from, say, a window by fitting a length of tubular heater immediately below the window.

The loading per cubic foot required for a room heated by

tubular heaters varies a great deal. A rough guide is 1 watt per cubic foot but, owing to the fact that the correct placing of the heaters affects the room temperature to a great extent, it is as well to consult the manufacturers.

Panel and Flood Heaters.—The low- and high-temperature types are suitable as permanent fixtures in living-rooms and bedrooms. The medium-temperature heaters can be either fixed or portable.

The low-temperature panel is either built into the wall, often underneath the plaster, or is screwed to the wall or ceiling. Medium-temperature panels can be conveniently applied as dado panels 3 feet long by 2 feet wide ; these are usually mounted away from the wall on brackets to permit circulation behind in addition to radiation from the front face. They may also be applied to the wall with thermal insulation behind. The surface temperature is 160°–170° F.

High-temperature panel heaters are carried on brackets at a slight angle from the wall, generally at a height of 7 or 8 feet, or, for heating very large rooms, the panels are suspended from ceilings by means of chains and hooks. Panels should be mounted so that their heat is radiated between the windows and the occupants of the room.

Underfloor Heating.—As indicated earlier, this may be either of the withdrawable or non-withdrawable type. It finds its greatest applications in industrial buildings where off-peak heating is encouraged. The heating cables are buried in the floor which is arranged to have a large thermal capacity. Supply to the installation is during the night when cheaper electricity is available, the heat being stored in the mass of concrete and then given out during the day. Heat loss to the walls and downwards is minimized by thermal insulation.

For the non-withdrawable system it is usual to install a slightly greater loading than required, so that if a section of the wire did become faulty it could be shorted out without overloading the remaining cable.

The cables are usually arranged to run from one side of a room to the other in a U-shaped configuration, with the spacing between adjacent cables varying according to the loading required.

Thermal Storage Heaters.—These take the form of slabs of concrete with the electric elements embedded in them. The concrete is covered by a suitable metal container so shaped as to look very much like a convector without the louvres. Since a heater weighs anything over 1 cwt., it is not a portable arrangement.

As with underfloor heating, this system makes use of the off-peak tariff, being time-switch and thermostatically controlled to reach its maximum temperature during the night and then radiate its stored heat during the day. It is available in 1 kW, 2 kW and 3 kW ratings.

Electricaire Heating.—This is an extremely flexible fan-operated warm air system giving rapid response so that close control of room temperature can be obtained. An important characteristic of this type of system is that heat can be delivered into selected rooms in a very short time. When the temperature is reached, the heater is left to operate under thermostatic control.

As these Electricaire heating units operate on the thermal storage principle, a small proportion of heat is always provided even when the fan is switched off. The heaters are available in two forms, as separate units suitable for individual room heating or as a central unit from which warm air is ducted as required to the areas served.

Infra-red Heaters.—These take the form of tubular elements mounted in suitably silvered reflectors. Ratings are available from 100 W to 4 kW at the normal industrial voltages. The element is usually surrounded by a ceramic tube made of pure fused silica quartz, the whole arrangement being capable of withstanding temperatures of the order of 1000° C. The heater operates in the 3 micron waveband and thus the element only reaches a black-heat.

Fan Heater.—One of the most efficient appliances for use in modern ventilating and air-conditioning is the electric fan heater. This consists essentially of a suitable heating element carried in a frame having an electric fan at the back and louvres at the front. When the fan is in operation and the heater element is switched on, heated air is distributed over a comparatively wide area of the room which it is desired to heat.

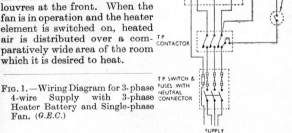

Fig. 1.—Wiring Diagram for 3-phase 4-wire Supply with 3-phase Heater Battery and Single-phase Fan. (*G.E.C.*)

307

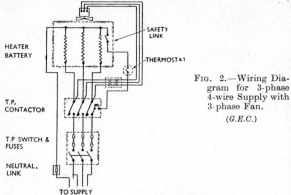

SAFETY
LINK

THERMOSTAT

T.P.
CONTACTOR

T.P SWITCH &
FUSES

NEUTRAL.
LINK

TO SUPPLY

Fig. 2.—Wiring Diagram for 3-phase 4-wire Supply with 3-phase Fan.

(*G.E.C.*)

For industrial use heaters are made in sizes from 5 to 20 kilowatts and for either single or three-phase.

It is recommended that three-phase supply should be utilized for the larger sizes of unit heater and three-phase fan, the load being equally distributed between the three phases. See Figs. 1 and 2.

The usual mounting height for these heaters is from 8 ft. to 9 ft. above ground level. Best results are obtained if thermostatic control is provided. The thermostat should for preference be fixed on the wall at a height of 6 ft. and well away from the unit heater which it is controlling. The method of connecting the thermostat in circuit is illustrated in Figs. 1 and 2.

It will be appreciated that the unit heater differs from the ordinary fire or radiator by virtue of the fact that a stream of comparatively cool air passes through the heating elements. This utilizes the principle of forced convection, thus greatly increasing the area over which the heat is distributed. In addition to this the electric unit heater system possesses the advantage that there are no stand-by losses, or maintenance costs, which form a necessary item in any system which depends upon a central heating boiler.

Thermostats.—All modern space-heating systems should be designed to take advantage of the convenience and economy which are provided by the thermostat. The best-known type utilizes a bi-metal strip, arranged in the form of a flat spiral. Further details will be found in the next section.

AUTOMATIC
TEMPERATURE CONTROL

THERMOSTATIC SWITCHES.

EXCEPT in a few special instruments, thermostatic switches operate either on the bi-metal principle, or on the vapour-pressure principle. In the former, the unequal expansion of two metals forming a composite strip causes distortion, which actuates the switch. In the latter, changes of vapour-pressure in a system charged with a volatile liquid causes expansion or contraction of a metallic bellows, which operates the switch.

For currents up to 10 or 15 amperes a.c. or 5 amperes d.c. at 250 volts open switches with silver contacts are standard practice. For heavier duty a mercury-tube switch is used.

TYPICAL APPLICATIONS

CONTROL OF SPACE HEATING.

(a) *Electric Heaters.*—Thermostat wired in series with the heaters (Fig. 1). If load is greater than the capacity of the thermostat, a relay or contactor must be used (Fig. 2).

(b) *Hot Water Circulation.*—Immersion thermostat in boiler to maintain constant water temperature by combustion control, e.g. motorized damper, and room thermostat to control room temperature by regulating circulation via a motorized valve.

DOMESTIC WATER SUPPLY.

(a) *Electric Water Heater.*—Immersion thermostat maintains constant water temperature by switching electric heating elements.

(b) *Steam Calorifier.*—Pressure-stat to maintain constant steam pressure by combustion control, e.g. by motorized damper or magnetic gas fuel valve, and immersion thermostat in calorifier to maintain constant water temperature by regulating steam flow (Fig. 3)

THERMOSTATIC CONTROL

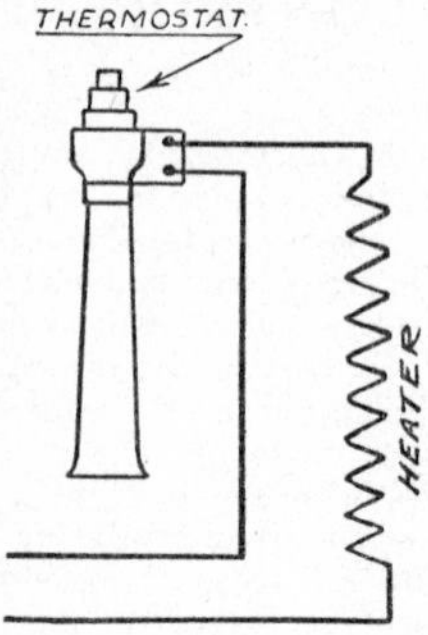

THERMOSTAT.

HEATER

FIG.1.

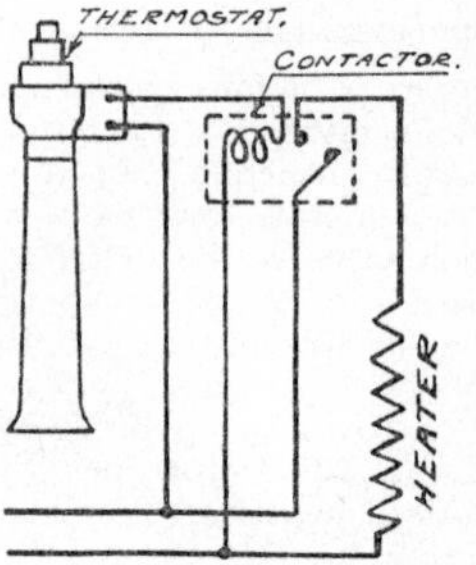

THERMOSTAT.

CONTACTOR.

HEATER

FIG.2.

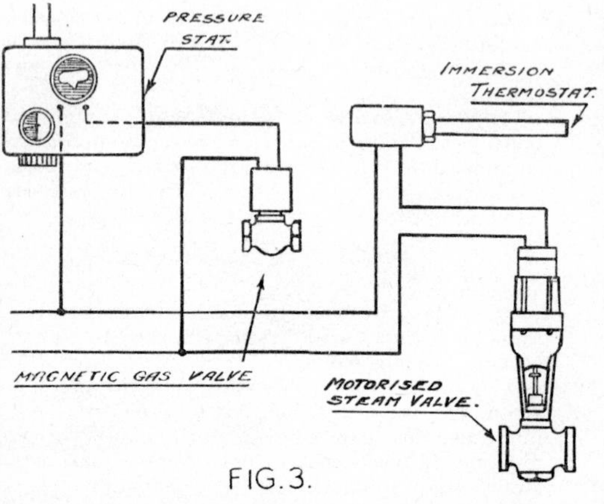

PRESSURE
STAT.

IMMERSION
THERMOSTAT.

MAGNETIC GAS VALVE

MOTORISED
STEAM VALVE.

FIG.3.

When the current is first turned on there is a very unpleasant smell, as the fine protective coating of grease and any oxides are burnt off. For this reason it is a very good practice to run the cooker at the contractor's workshop for a short time to avoid this taking place in the user's kitchen.

Preparing the Site.—Every electric cooker must be controlled from a main switch adjacent to the cooker so that the whole appliance may be dead for cleaning. Main switches are of two types, those with the switch handle at the side and those with the switch handle at the front projecting through the cover plate. In addition the main switch in which the switch handle projects from the front is generally fitted with a visual signal, this being either a mechanically operated flag or an indicating lamp, and a 3-pin plug and single-pole switch for a kettle or iron. The whole arrangement is termed a cooker-control unit.

As the cooker is already equipped with main and sub-circuit fuses it is not necessary to provide main fuses in the main switch, but a single-pole fuse is generally incorporated mounted in the live main to protect the indicating lamp and 3-pin plug.

The main switch should first be connected to incoming supply. Note that the terminals are clearly marked " live " and " neutral," and it is important that the correct mains should be connected to these terminals.

Wherever possible v.r.i. cables in conduit should be used. A cooker load is one in which the whole of the elements may quite conceivably be on together, and the size of cables should be adequate for the full load.

Connecting Cooker to Main Switch.—The next step is to connect the cooker to the main switch, and for this purpose v.r.i. cable in flexible metallic conduit is preferable. It will be appreciated that occasions will arise when it may be desirable to move the cooker slightly for the purpose of cleaning behind it, and it would not be advisable to run the connections between the cooker and main switch in inflexible protective covering.

The v.r.i. cables are connected to the outer two terminals of the main switch, the other ends being connected to the terminals at the bottom of the cooker. The lead from the live side of the switch must be connected to the upper terminal or, in cookers where the terminals are differently placed, to the one leading direct to the distribution fuses.

Earthing.—Care must be taken to see that the cooker and main switch are efficiently earthed, either through the

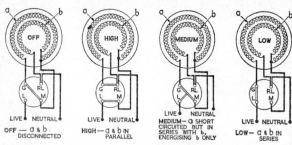

FIG. 1.—Diagram of Connections for 3-heat Switch.

conduit and flexible metallic tubing where this is used or through separate earth leads where lead-covered cable or plastics conduit is used. The use of the lead sheath as an earth connection is not to be recommended except as a last resource.

Cooker Control.—The two most common methods of heat control are the "3-heat switch" and the "Simmerstat" controller. The following notes are given to help the installation engineer who may not be familiar with these devices.

The 3-heat Switch Control comprises two elements which, according to the method of connection to the supply, give three heating effects, i.e. "high" (full rating), "medium" (half rating) and "low" (quarter rating). When the switch is in the "high" position the two heating elements, each rated at 1,000 watts, are connected in parallel across the supply ; but when the switch is turned to the "medium" position only one element is energized so that the oven or grille is now operating at half its full rating. With the switch in the "low" position both heating elements are connected in series across the supply and a simple calculation will show that the power is again reduced by one-half.

The "Simmerstat" Controller is shown in Fig. 2. Here the heat control is obtained (given a certain amount of heat storage as in a boiling plate) by periodically interrupting the circuit. If a boiling plate is switched on for, say, ten seconds and then switched off for ten seconds repeatedly, over a period the amount of energy consumed is, of course, half that consumed if switched on full all the time, giving half, or "medium" heat. If the ratio of on-and-off periods is altered to give five seconds on and fifteen seconds off the result is " low " or quarter heat. Two seconds on and eighteen seconds off would be one-tenth heat, and so on.

By turning the control knob up or down, any desired variation in energy fed to the boiling plate is achieved. The periodical operation of the switch contacts is effected by a bi-metallic strip which is made to move by a minute amount of heat applied to it by a very small heating element. When the strip has reached the end of its travel it opens a pair of contacts, breaking the circuit to the heating elements. The strip cools and resumes its former position when the contacts close again, and the cycle of movement is repeated indefinitely.

If a boiling plate is connected in parallel with the controlling

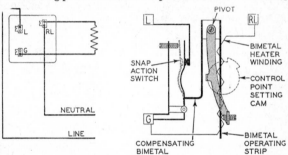

Fig. 2.—Diagrams showing Construction and Connections for Type TYC " Simmerstat " Control.

heating element it, too, will be subject to the periodic application of energy and by varying the distance of travel of the bi-metallic strip, by turning the control knob, any desired ratio of on-and-off periods can be obtained. The control knob is numbered from 0 to 5 with an " off " position below the 0. Full heat is obtained when the control is turned to 5, the switch contacts remaining together continuously, but as soon as the control is turned to about 4 the contacts begin to interrupt the circuit periodically, and heat is reduced to about one-half as variation is not required above this amount. An even and smooth reduction of heat is obtained by further turning the control towards zero, at which point the heat input is reduced to approximately 8 per cent. This is equivalent to about 150 watts, with an 1,800-watt boiling plate, reducing heat input to a saucepan well below simmering point.

HIGH-FREQUENCY HEATING

OF the many developments in electric heating during the last several years, probably the most important has been the adaption of high-frequency electricity for the purpose of heating various materials. This is carried out with the use of electrical energy which alternates at frequencies normally used for radio transmission and reception.

The conversion of the normal 50-cycle a.c. supply to radio frequencies is carried out by a radio valve generator, which is similar in principle and construction to a radio transmitter. The generator must be adequately screened to prevent radio interference.

Types of H.F. Heating.—There are two distinct types of radio or high-frequency heating:

(1) Dielectric heating for non-conductors of heat, such as plastics, glues, wood, rubber, asbestos, clay, foods, etc., the basic principles of which have been known and established for many years in medical diathermy.

(2) Eddy-current heating for metals, which has been used for some time in the induction furnace, but at much lower frequencies.

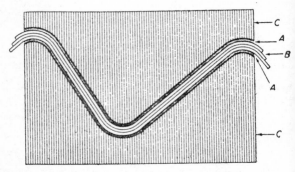

FIG. 1.—Dielectric Heating of Laminated Board (B) between Copper Plates (A) connected to Radio Heater and held in Jig (C).

delivers to a port in the magnetic valve, and the discharge of water through the magnetic valve may therefore be either water from within the feed reservoir, or that being delivered by the pump or a combination of the two.

Within two or three minutes steam will be generated and, provided the amount of steam drawn off is less than the capacity for which the boiler is set, the pressure will rise. When the pressure in the boiler approaches the setting pressure modulator, the latter operates and takes over the control of the load relay ; with rising pressure the modulator reduces the setting of this relay progressively until the boiler loading balances the steam requirement and prevents any further rise of pressure in the boiler. Similarly, if the pressure starts to drop, the modulator resets the load relay progressively for greater loads, thus at all times maintaining a balance between the load of the boiler and the steam requirements. The pressure variation for control between full and minimum load can be as close as one or two p.s.i. The changes in load of the boiler are effected very quickly, taking only a matter of one or two minutes to go from no load to full load, and vice versa.

Should a very rapid pressure-increase occur in the boiler, due, for example, to instantaneous closing of the main steam-valve, the modulator not only selects a minimum setting for the load relay, but, at the same time, it stops the feed pump so that no further water is delivered, and if practically no steam is required it energizes the magnetic valve directly and reduces the load on the boiler to zero.

Feed Water Temp.	Pounds of Steam per Hour per kW.					
	At 5 lb/ sq. in.	At 15 lb/ sq. in.	At 40 lb/ sq. in.	At 80 lb/ sq. in.	At 120 lb/ sq. in.	At 150 lb/ sq. in.
50° F	2·85	2·83	2·81	2·79	2·77	2·75
100° F	2·98	2·96	2·94	2·92	2·90	2·88
150° F	3·13	3·10	3·07	3·04	3·02	3·00
200° F	3·29	3·26	3·23	3·20	3·18	3·17

On a heavy steam demand the boiler will be controlled by the load control relay. Should the steam demand be reduced the control will be taken over by the pressure regulators which reduce the loading to the value required.

RADIANT HEAT DRYING

MANY radio and television receiver cabinets and many items of furniture are finished with cellulose lacquer. This finishing process usually consists of several distinct operations, a typical schedule being as follows :

   (1) Apply an oil-based stain filler ;
   (2) Air dry ;
   (3) Spray with cellulose-based sanding sealer
   (4) Air dry ;
   (5) Rub down and respray ;
   (6) Air dry ;
   (7) Apply first coat of lacquer;
   (8) Air dry ;
   (9) Apply second coat ;
 (10) Air dry ;
 (11) Rub down with fine abrasive paper and smoothing
       agent ;
 (12) Air dry ;
 (13) Burnish.

As the air-drying periods between the processes vary from half an hour to eight hours, it will be seen that in order to follow out this finishing schedule a very considerable time must be allowed for the drying processes. By using radiant heat the drying time can be shortened very considerably.

The radiant heating plants used for this work are in the form of tunnels made up of rows of lamps and reflectors which are positioned 12–18 inches from the nearest part of the article being treated (Fig. 1). The lamps are of the standard 115-volt, 250-watt internal reflector pattern used for stoving metal finishes, but the intensities in the tunnels are much lower. Thus whereas flux densities of radiation equivalent to power inputs to the lamps of up to 1,000 watts per square foot of tunnel surface area are commonly used for stoving metal finishes, the corresponding figure for cellulose wood finishes is 200 watts per square foot. This reduced intensity is obtained by spacing the lamps well apart or by running them at reduced voltage.

A radiant heating plant of fixed lamp and reflector contour has considerable versatility. Thus one contour is satisfactory for all sizes of radio and television cabinets and

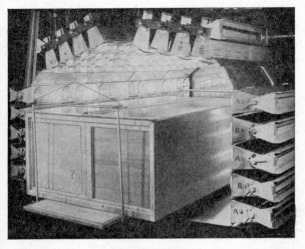

FIG. 1.—Lamp Tunnel for Drying the Cellulose Finish on
Wardrobes.

(*G.E.C.*)

another will handle all items of bedroom furniture : wardrobes, dressing tables, tallboys, chests of drawers and bed
ends. In general, the uniformity of drying over all surfaces
of these articles is very good, though the inner vertical surfaces of "well" type dressing tables (which are partly
shadowed) are slower to dry than the other surfaces.

In an actual production plant where this method has been
adopted, the total drying time required for completing the
schedule has been reduced from $18\frac{1}{2}$ hours to 2 hours,
40 minutes.

ELECTRIC REFRIGERATION

THE majority of electrically driven refrigerators for domestic use are of the compressor type. A suitable gas, such as freon or methyl chloride, is compressed by an electrically driven compressor. During compression the temperature of the gas rises. The gas passes from the outlet side of the compressor through cooling coils, which may be air- or water-cooled ; usually the latter. The cooling combined with the high pressure liquefies the gas which then passes in liquid form to the evaporator. This is really the freezing chamber or freezing unit of the refrigerator. It is in passing through this unit that the liquid refrigerant takes up heat. It is subjected to suction pressure from the suction side of the compressor. This causes the liquid to boil and in doing so it absorbs latent heat, thus producing a low temperature around and inside the refrigerating unit. A thermostat switch is provided to maintain the refrigeration chamber at any desired temperature within its working limits. The scheme is shown diagrammatically in Fig. 1.

In the sealed unit which is now widely used in domestic refrigerators, the compressor and the motor are placed together inside a hermetically sealed container. The motor windings, therefore, become saturated with liquid refrigerant and oil and great care has to be exercised to use materials which will not disintegrate in the slightest degree and cause sludge which would block the system. No sparking can be allowed and, therefore, the motor must be of the squirrel-cage type. Since the motor must be of the split-phase type and a centrifugal switch cannot be used, it is necessary either to use an external magnetic switch to cut out the starting winding, or to arrange an unloading device on the compressor so that only a small starting torque is required. In this design the refrigerator unit ceases to be an assembly of various individual components, and becomes virtually a single piece of mechanism. From this it follows that except for minor adjustments in regard to such things as the thermostat, there is only one service operation in the case of trouble, and that is to remove the complete unit and put in another one.

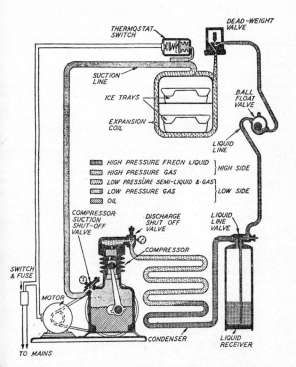

FIG. 1.—Diagrammatic Arrangement of Compressor Type Electrical Refrigerator.

The refrigerant gas is drawn into the compressor inlet and passes out under high pressure and at a moderately high temperature. It passes through a condenser or cooling coil where it liquefies. The liquid then passes into the refrigerating coil or expansion coil, the outlet of which is in communication with the suction line of the compressor. Under the influence of the reduced pressure the refrigerant vaporizes and takes up latent heat, thus reducing the temperature of the refrigerating chamber to the required point.

325

THEORY OF MEASURING INSTRUMENTS

MOST instruments and meters are based on either the magnetic principle or that of electro-magnetic induction. In addition, there are a number of other instruments which make use of electrostatic, heating and chemical effects, each of these having a special application or applications.

AMMETERS AND VOLTMETERS

The normal instruments for measuring current and voltage are essentially the same in principle, as in most cases the deflection is proportional to the current passing through the instrument. These meters are, therefore, all ammeters, but in the case of a voltmeter the scale is such that the reading is proportional to the voltage across the instrument.

The types of instrument used are :

1. Moving iron (suitable for both a.c. and d.c.).
2. Permanent magnet moving coil (suitable for d.c. only).
3. Dynamometer type (moving coil) (suitable for both a.c. and d.c.).
4. Electrostatic (for a.c. and d.c. voltmeters).
5. Induction (suitable for a.c. only).
6. Hot wire (suitable for a.c. and d.c.).

Note.—The permanent-magnet moving-coil instrument can be used for a.c., provided a rectifier is incorporated, and this is described in another section.

Accuracy.

The accuracy of instruments used for measuring current and voltage will naturally vary with the type and quality of manufacture, and various grades of meters have been scheduled by the British Standards Institution. These are set out in the British Standard No. 89 (1954).

There are two grades of instruments, precision and industrial. These grades enable an engineer to purchase instruments with an accuracy sufficient for the purpose for which the instrument is intended.

For normal use industrial instruments are sufficiently

Fig. 1.—Platform Scale Ammeter.

(*Nalder Bros. & Thompson Ltd.*)

accurate. Instruments are grouped in these grades by virtue of the permissible errors which are set out in the specification.

Many manufacturers are now producing indicating instruments, such as ammeters, voltmeters and wattmeters, with a platform scale (see Fig. 1). With this type of instrument the pointer traverses an arc in the same plane as the actual scale markings, thus eliminating side shadow and parallax error.

MOVING-IRON INSTRUMENTS

This type of instrument is in general use in industry owing to its cheap first cost and its reliability. Although suitable for use on both a.c. and d.c. it has naturally been developed more for use on a.c. There are two types of moving-iron instruments—the attraction type and the repulsion type, the latter being in more common use than the former.

The principle of operation is that a coil of wire carrying the current to be measured attracts or repels an armature of " soft " iron, which operates the indicating needle or pointer. With the attraction type the iron is drawn into the coil by means of the current ; and in the repulsion type there are two pieces of iron inside the coil, one of these being fixed and the other movable. Both these are magnetized

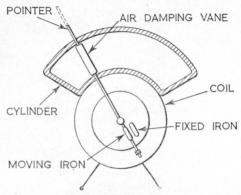

POINTER

AIR DAMPING VANE

COIL

CYLINDER

FIXED IRON

MOVING IRON

Fig. 2.—Moving-Iron Instrument—Repulsion Type.

by the current and the repulsion between the two causes the movable unit to operate the pointer.

It will be seen, therefore, that the direction of current in the coil does not matter, making the instrument suitable for measuring any form of current, either d.c. or a.c., including rectified a.c. with any wave form.

Causes of Error.

(a) *Stray Magnetic Fields.*—Owing to the fact that the deflection is proportional to the magnetic field inside the operating coil, magnetic fields due to any outside source will affect the deflection. Errors due to this are reduced by suitable magnetic screening of the mechanism.

(b) *Hysteresis.*—Even with the most suitable iron there is a certain amount of hysteresis, which causes readings to vary to some extent. Errors due to hysteresis are kept low by designing the armature so that it is not too large and has a fairly low flux density.

(c) *Frequency.*—Due to the frequency of the circuit changing the reactance, different readings will be obtained on different frequencies and there is also an effect due to eddy currents.

As frequency is now standardized this is not important, and where necessary a capacitor can be used to make the instrument practically independent of frequency.

For lower voltages from 400 V to a few thousand volts the *quadrant* type is used, the principle being as in Fig. 5. The moving vane is pivoted and is either repelled or attracted or both by the charges on the vane and the quadrants—these charges being proportional to the potential due to their connection to the supply.

In commercial models several sets of vanes are used in parallel to obtain sufficient torque.

Voltages of 100 kV and over are measured by means of two shaped discs with an air-space between them, one disc being fixed and the other movable axially. By means of a balance the force between the two is measured and the scale of the balance marked in kilovolts. These voltmeters are not, of course, accurate to a degree that makes them suitable for indicating line voltages or for switchboard purposes. They are, however, ideal for testing purposes where cables and other apparatus is subject to high-voltage and destruction tests. In this case they form a visual indication of the applied voltage and are a check on the value indicated by the instruments on the voltage *stepping up* apparatus.

Electrostatic instruments for laboratory use are termed *electrometers* and are usually of the suspension type with mirror-operated scales.

As these instruments do not consume any power whatever, they have the advantage that they do not affect the state of any circuit to which they are connected. There is a very small current flowing on a.c., but this is negligible in nearly all cases. The exception is of course in the case of radio-frequency measurements.

HOT-WIRE INSTRUMENTS

The current to be measured, or a known fraction of it, is passed through a fine wire and, due to the heating effect of the current, the wire expands. If the resistance and coefficient of expansion of the wire is constant, then the heating and consequent expansion of the wire are both directly proportional to the square of the current. If the expansion is sufficient by suitable connections as shown in Fig. 6, it can be made to move the pointer. This movement is also proportional to the square of the current. By suitable scaling the current can thus be determined.

Since such instruments obey the square law they are suitable for both d.c. and a.c. systems. Furthermore, since they only operate on the heating effect, the r.m.s. value of an alternating current is measured irrespective of frequency or wave form. They are also unaffected by stray magnetic fields.

INDUCTION INSTRUMENTS

These instruments, which will function only on a.c., may be used for ammeters and voltmeters, but their use for the measurement of these two quantities is much less than for wattmeters and energy meters—these applications being described fully below.

In all induction instruments the torque of the moving system is due to the reaction of a flux produced by the current to be measured on the eddy currents flowing in a metal disc or cylinder, this latter flux also being due to the current but arranged to be out of phase with the former flux.

There are two methods by which these fluxes are obtained. With a cylindrical rotor two sets of coils can be used at right angles, or with a disc rotor the shaded pole principle is used, an alternative being the use of two magnetic fields acting on the disc.

Although extremely simple, with no connections to the rotor, these instruments have many disadvantages which prevent their use for general purposes as ammeters and voltmeters. The points in their favour are a long scale, good damping and freedom from stray field effects. Their disadvantages include fairly serious errors due to variation in frequency and temperature, high power consumption, and their high cost. The former may be reduced by suitable compensation, but in ordinary commercial instruments the variation is still important, although first-grade instruments can be supplied if required.

WATTMETERS

Dynamometer Wattmeters.—This type of wattmeter will give correct readings both on d.c. and a.c., and consists of a stationary circuit carrying the current and a moving circuit representing the voltage of the circuit. For laboratory instruments the meter may be either of the suspended coil or pivoted coil type. The former is used as a standard wattmeter, but the pivoted coil has a much wider scope as it is suitable for direct indicating.

For accurate measurements it is necessary to compensate

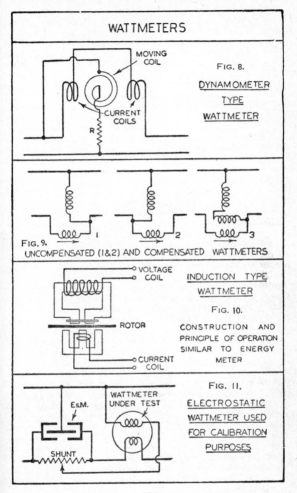

WATTMETERS

FIG. 8.
DYNAMOMETER TYPE WATTMETER

MOVING COIL

CURRENT COILS

R

FIG. 9.
UNCOMPENSATED (1&2) AND COMPENSATED WATTMETERS

1   2   3

INDUCTION TYPE WATTMETER

FIG. 10.

VOLTAGE COIL

ROTOR

CURRENT COIL

CONSTRUCTION AND PRINCIPLE OF OPERATION SIMILAR TO ENERGY METER

FIG. 11.
ELECTROSTATIC WATTMETER USED FOR CALIBRATION PURPOSES

E.S.M.

SHUNT

WATTMETER UNDER TEST

335

for the flow of current in the other circuit by adding a compensating winding to the current circuit. This will be seen from the diagram on page 335, where the connections (1) and (2) will introduce errors due to the extra current in the current coil in (1) and the volt-drop in the current coil in (2). It will be seen that the arrangement in (3) overcomes these errors.

In addition to errors caused by the inductance of the voltage circuit, dynamometer wattmeters are affected by stray fields. This is true for both d.c. and a.c. measurements, but on a.c. only alternating current stray fields affect readings. This effect is avoided by using astatic construction for laboratory instruments and by shielding for portable types. The use of a nickel-iron of high permeability has enabled modern wattmeters to be practically unaffected by stray fields in general use.

When purchasing wattmeters of this type it is desirable to see that a high factor of safety is used as regards the rating of the coils of the instrument. This is desirable from the point of possible overload on any of the ranges of a multi-range instrument, but it also enables the indication to be made towards full-scale even at low power-factors.

For 3-phase wattmeters, adequate shielding between the two sections is necessary, but even then they do not give the same accuracy as single-phase models.

Induction Wattmeters.—These can only be used on a.c. and are similar to energy meters of the induction type, the rotating disc in this case operating against a torsion spring. The two circuits are similar to the induction energy meter and the connections are as shown on page 335.

Although affected by variations in temperature and frequency, the former is compensated for by the variation in resistance of the rotating disc (which is opposite in effect to the effect on the windings), and the latter does not vary considerably with the variations in frequency which usually obtain. Induction wattmeters must not, of course, be used on any other frequency than that for which they are designed unless specially arranged with suitable tappings.

The general construction of induction wattmeters renders them reliable and robust. They have a definite advantage for switchboard use in that the scale may be over an arc of 300° or so. As with dynamometer types, the 3-phase 2-element wattmeter is not as accurate as the single-phase type.

Three-phase Wattmeters.—These operate on the two wattmeter principle, the two rotors being mechanically coupled to give the sum of the torques of the two elements. As already stated, it is important to avoid any interference between the two sections, and there are several methods of preventing this. One is to use a compensating resistance in the connections to the pressure coils, and another, due to Drysdale, is to mount the two moving coils (of the dynamometer type) at right angles.

Measurement of Three-phase Power.—The connections of temporarily-connected instruments for measuring three-phase power are given on page 77. Most portable watt-meters are designed for a maximum current of 5 amps., and

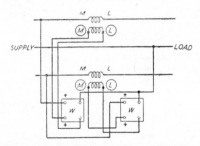

FIG. 12.—Two-wattmeter Method of Measuring 3-phase Power.

are used with current transformers. If two such wattmeters with transformers are connected as in Fig. 12, the algebraic sum of the wattmeter readings multiplied by the transformer ratio will give the total power in a three-phase circuit.

In most tests of the power consumption of three-phase motors, one wattmeter will give sufficient accuracy if it is properly connected, because motor loads are very approximately balanced. In this case, the total three-phase power is three times the wattmeter reading multiplied by the transformer ratio. If the supply is 3-wire without a neutral, two current transformers are required, but three-phase supply usually includes a neutral for lighting circuits. If the power installation is supplied from a local substation in the works, the earthed point of the neutral will be, electrically, very near the testing position. In this condition three-phase power may be measured in balanced circuits by connecting the wattmeter voltage circuit between the line supplying the current coil of the instrument and earth. The earth connection is electrically equivalent to a connection to the supply neutral. When the power installation is some distance from the substation, there may be a considerable difference of potential between the neutral of the supply and earth. In this case, the following method is very convenient: Connect one voltage terminal of the wattmeter to the line in the usual way ; to the other terminal join a single lead connected to one of the terminals of a lampholder adaptor. By inserting the adaptor into a switched-off lampholder, the voltage circuit can be joined to the supply neutral in the holder.

VALVE VOLTMETERS

THESE essentially consist of a thermionic valve which has a milliammeter connected in its anode circuit. The voltage which is to be measured is normally applied to its control grid circuit, which imposes very little load on the circuit, even at a high frequency. Although the basic arrangement of a valve voltmeter has a limited range, this can be extended by the use of a potential divider.

As already noted above, the valve voltmeter takes practically no power at all from the source under test, and this factor is an important one in the measurement of voltages in a radio circuit. An ordinary moving coil meter, no matter how sensitive it may be, always draws some power from the circuit under test. In circuits where there is plenty of power available this is not serious, but when dealing with a circuit in which even a load of a few microamperes would seriously affect the accuracy of the reading, a valve voltmeter should be used.

When comparing the load imposed upon an a.c. circuit by a moving-coil voltmeter and a valve voltmeter, it is also necessary to consider the frequency since a moving-coil meter is very frequency conscious. By this it is meant that the instrument in the first place is calibrated at a particular frequency and will only measure alternating current accurately at this frequency. An important advantage of the valve voltmeter is that it may be designed to cover practically any frequency ; commercially manufactured instruments are suitable for frequencies up to 50 Mc/s and above.

Secondly, the valve voltmeter will often be used on circuits where the voltage is not very high so that its input impedance can only be compared with a moving-coil meter which has been adjusted to the appropriate range. This means that it is usually impossible to determine accurately a low voltage on the high voltage range of a moving-coil meter. On the other hand, the valve voltmeter maintains a high impedance over all its ranges and is, in fact, the only type of instrument that can be used for low-voltage R.F. measurements.

A further application of the thermionic valve to voltage measurement is to be found in the diode peak voltmeter. When an instrument of this type is connected to an a.c. source, rectification takes place in the diode each half-wave surge charging a capacitor in the output circuit to the peak value of the wave. Provided the voltmeter in the circuit is of sufficiently high resistance and is large enough to prevent a loss of charge through the meter when the rectifier is not passing current, the reading on the meter will indicate the peak voltage, irrespective of the waveform.

It is an important point to note that either a.c. only, d.c. only or a.c. and d.c. can be measured on the various types of valve voltmeter in use today. An a.c. valve voltmeter which has a blocking capacitor incorporated in its input circuit cannot be used for measuring d.c. However, it is not a difficult matter to short-circuit the capacitor when it is necessary for a d.c. measurement to be taken.

Because of the steady potential on the grid in the case of d.c. the calibration will be affected. In this case a resistance is sometimes inserted between the d.c. input terminal and the range potential divider to compensate for the rise in sensitivity so that the calibration of the meter is similar for both a.c. and d.c. measurements.

SHUNTS AND SERIES RESISTANCES

THE control or reduction of the actual currents flowing in the various circuits of an instrument or meter may be obtained either by means of resistances (for both d.c. and a.c.) or by the use of instrument transformers (a.c. only).

Shunts.—Non-inductive resistances for increasing the range of ammeters are termed shunts and are connected as shown in Fig. 1. The relative values to give any required result can be seen as follows, the symbols being marked on the diagram :

Let R = resistance of ammeter
r = resistance of shunt
I = total current in circuit
i_a = current in ammeter
i_s = current in shunt.

We have $I = i_a + i_s$, and as the volt-drop across the meter and the shunt are the same we get

$$i_a R = i_s r$$

$$\therefore i_a = i_s \frac{r}{R} = I \frac{r}{R + r}$$

or

$$I = i_a \frac{R + r}{r}$$

$$= i_a \left(\frac{R}{r} + 1 \right)$$

The expression $\left(\frac{R}{r} + 1 \right)$ is termed the *multiplying power* of the shunt.

As an example, take the case of a meter reading to 5 amps. having a resistance of 0·02 ohm. Find a suitable shunt for use on circuits up to 100 amps.

As the total current has to be $\frac{100}{5}$ = 20 times that through the meter, the shunt must carry 19 times. Thus its resistance must be $\frac{1}{19}$ that of the meter, giving a shunt whose resistance is $\frac{0·02}{19}$ or 0·00105 ohm.

Series Resistances.—In the case of voltmeters it is often impracticable to allow the whole voltage to be taken to the coil or coils of the instrument. For instance, in the case of a moving-coil voltmeter the current in the moving coil will

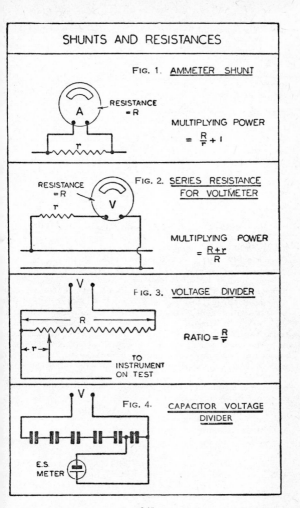

SHUNTS AND RESISTANCES

FIG. 1. AMMETER SHUNT

RESISTANCE = R

MULTIPLYING POWER $= \frac{R}{r} + 1$

FIG. 2. SERIES RESISTANCE FOR VOLTMETER

RESISTANCE = R

MULTIPLYING POWER $= \frac{R+r}{R}$

FIG. 3. VOLTAGE DIVIDER

R

TO INSTRUMENT ON TEST

RATIO $= \frac{R}{r}$

FIG. 4. CAPACITOR VOLTAGE DIVIDER

E.S METER

be in the nature of 0·01 amp. and its resistance will probabl[y]
be only 100 ohms. If this instrument is to be used for, sa[y]
100 volts, a series resistance will be essential—connected a[s]
shown in Fig. 2.

The relation between total voltage and that of th[e]
meter is simple as the two voltages are in series. Thus i[n]
the above case the full-scale current will be 0·01 amp., s[o]
that the total resistance for 100 volts will have to be $\frac{100}{0\cdot01}$ o[r]
10,000 ohms. If the resistance of the meter circuit and it[s]
connecting leads is 100 ohms, then the added or serie[s]
resistance must be 10,000 − 100 = 9,900 ohms.

The multiplying power is the ratio between the tot[al]
voltage across the instrument and that across the coil only. [If]

R = resistance of meter
r = value of series resistance

then multiplying power = $\frac{R + r}{R}$

Construction of Shunts and Series Resistances.—
Shunts usually consist of manganin strips soldered to tw[o]
terminal blocks at each end and arranged so that air wi[ll]
circulate between the strips for cooling.

As with an ammeter shunt, the impedance of the serie[s]
resistance used in a voltmeter must remain constant fo[r]
differing frequencies, i.e. the inductance must not vary. Fo[r]
this reason the resistance-coils (of manganin) are ofte[n]
wound upon flat mica strips to reduce the area enclosed by th[e]
wire, and hence reduce the enclosed flux for a given curren[t].

Voltage Dividers.—Voltage dividers or volt-boxes ca[n]
only be used with accuracy with testing equipment o[r]
measuring instruments which do not take any current, o[r]
with electrostatic instruments. The former state of affair[s]
refers to tests using the " null " or zero deflection for balancin[g]
or taking a reading while the electrostatic meter actuall[y]
does not take any current.

The principle of the voltage divider is seen in Fig. [3.]
The voltage to be measured is connected across a resistance [R]
and the connections are taken off some fraction of th[is]
resistance as shown. The ratio is given by $\frac{R}{r}$.

A similar arrangement is possible with capacitors for us[e]
with electrostatic instruments, but the method is somewha[t]
complicated owing to the variation in capacity of the instru[-]
ment as the vane or vanes move.

ENERGY METERS

KILOWATT-HOUR meters were developed in the early days of the supply industry because it was most important to be able to accurately measure the energy supplied to a consumer. Many types were invented and several principles of operation were utilized, but in all cases the devices are based on the fact that the rate of registration can be made closely proportional to the power being supplied. Since energy is the integral of power with respect to time it will be appreciated why the registration is proportional to the energy supplied and why electricity meters are called integrating meters.

Direct-current meters have a limited use in this country, but there still remains some demand in export markets. Only one type of meter is now in general use and this is the mercury-motor type, the principles of which are described below.

For alternating current integrating meters the induction disc principle has been generally adopted.

Mercury-Motor Meters.—The direct current is passed through a copper disc in the region where it is cut by the magnetic flux of a strong permanent magnet, and the consequent torque, which is proportional to the current, causes the disc to revolve. The current is led in and out of the copper disc by immersing the disc in a bath of mercury and placing suitable electrodes at two points of the bath wall.

The motion of the disc is controlled by the eddy current braking effect of the copper disc cutting the flux of the permanent magnet or magnets. Consequently the speed of the disc is closely proportional to the current passing through the meter because the braking torque is proportional to the disc speed since the braking flux is constant.

It should be mentioned here that all motor meters make use of the eddy current brake owing to its ideal property of being proportional to the disc speed. Every motor, however, possesses some friction and this is usually the greatest difficulty in making meters accurate on all loads. Unfortunately the mercury motor meter cannot be easily compensated for the effect of friction and thus its performance on low loads is not very efficient.

343

There are two distinct types of mercury-motor meter. The single magnet type, which is operated as an ampere-hour meter, has its field provided by a powerful permanent magnet. In the second type, the field is provided by an electro-magnet energized from the mains voltage. This type is known as the mercury-motor watt-hour meter.

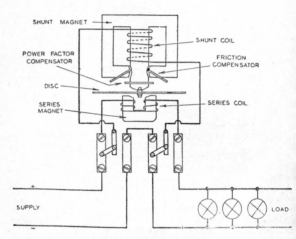

FIG. 1.—Electrical Circuits of a Typical Induction Meter.

Induction Meters.—The popular single-phase induction meter consists fundamentally of two electro-magnets, an aluminium disc, a revolution counter, and a brake magnet connected to the load as shown in Fig. 1. Fig. 2 shows how the coils are connected to create two a.c. fluxes cutting the disc—one proportional to the voltage and the other proportional to the current being measured. Each of these fluxes induces eddy currents in the disc. It is due to the interaction of the voltage flux with the eddy currents created by the current flux, and to the interaction of the current flux with the eddy currents created by the voltage flux, that a torque is exerted on the disc, causing it to rotate. The purpose of the permanent magnet is simply to act as an

344

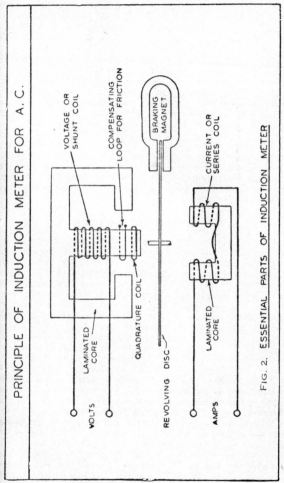

PRINCIPLE OF INDUCTION METER FOR A.C.

VOLTAGE OR SHUNT COIL

COMPENSATING LOOP FOR FRICTION

BRAKING MAGNET

CURRENT OR SERIES COIL

LAMINATED CORE

QUADRATURE COIL

VOLTS

REVOLVING DISC

LAMINATED CORE

AMPS

FIG. 2. ESSENTIAL PARTS OF INDUCTION METER

eddy current brake on the motion of the disc so as to make the disc speed proportional to the power being measured. The voltage element is specially compensated by a quadrature adjuster so that the meter will be reasonably accurate at all power factors.

The induction meter is remarkable on account of the multiplicity of ways in which the electro-magnets and compensating devices can be arranged to give similar results, and on account of the high accuracy of measurement which can be achieved. Owing to the induction principle the mechanical construction is of the simplest possible type with a resulting freedom from frictional troubles and low maintenance requirements. Furthermore, the effect of friction is compensated by means of a special compensator which provides a driving torque irrespective of the load current.

In order to meter two- or three-phase supplies two or more elements are arranged so as to drive the same rotor system. The elements may operate on one disc or on separate discs mounted on a common shaft.

TESTING OF METERS

It is not practicable to test meters under working conditions, and it is therefore customary to use phantom loads for testing purposes. The current and voltage circuits are usually supplied from independent sources, and this enables the current to be supplied at a low voltage with consequent savings in energy, apparatus and test-room working conditions. So long as the conditions in the meter reproduce the working conditions it is obviously immaterial how the testing currents and voltages are derived.

D.C. mercury-motor meters are normally tested on battery circuits. The test circuit is supplied by a low-voltage battery with regulating resistances connected in series to give the range of currents required.

Single-phase a.c. meters are usually tested on transformer circuits such as that shown on Fig. 4. A.C. circuits, however, vary in nature considerably according to the ideas of the designer, particularly polyphase testing circuits.

Meters vary widely in their detail testing requirements, but the general scheme is to test them at a high load, a low load and an intermediate load.

Under the Electricity Supply (Meters) Act 1936, which governs the testing of electricity meters, for single-phase two-wire whole current a.c. meters the high- and low-load

ELECTRIC WELDING

THERE are two main types of electric welding, namely:

    (a) Arc welding.
    (b) Resistance welding.

These may be further subdivided as below:

Arc Welding.

    1. D.C. metallic arc welding.
    2. A.C. metallic arc welding.
    3. Carbon arc welding, which may be either d.c. or a.c.
    4. Atomic hydrogen welding.
    5. Inert-gas shielded arc welding (Argonarc).

Resistance Welding.

    1. Butt welding.
    2. Butt seam welding.
    3. Lap seam welding.
    4. Spot welding.
    5. Projection welding.
    6. Flash welding.

ARC WELDING

Here again the types of equipment used may be broadly classified under two distinct headings.

D.C. Welding Equipment.—D.C. welding equipment consists of a motor-generator or engine-generator set, and accessories.

Where a direct-current supply is available, a motor generator set may be installed, the motor being wound to suit the voltage of the local electric power mains. It is recommended that multiples of single- and/or double-operator sets, comprising dynamos of the drooping voltage type, should be used for the following reasons:

When a number of single- or double-operator plants are in operation, there is no risk of a *total* shut-down of the welding shops in case of breakdown.

Consumption of electric power will be considerably less than

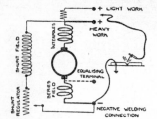

FIG. 1.—Wiring Diagram
showing Terminals of
Single-Operator Type
Welding Set.

that of a multi-operator machine of the level compound-
wound type for a given number of welders in each case.

The smaller units, being usually self-contained, can be
easily moved to positions most convenient for the work in
hand.

There is no possibility of electrical interference between
operators (many level characteristic machines give trouble in
this respect).

The length of heavy welding cables is reduced to a minimum, as each machine can be placed near the job.

They can be paralleled when required to give larger currents
to one welder.

Against the above is the question of initial cost of a number
of single- or double-operator sets, but this is offset by lower
running costs and the many other advantages enumerated
above.

Welding Dynamo Characteristics.—Fig. 1 shows diagrammatically the arrangement for d.c. arc welding. The
welding generator is, of course, a low-voltage heavy-current
machine with drooping characteristic, see Fig. 2. As the
characteristics required for different types of welds differ, it
is usual to provide in welding generators a means of altering
the characteristic curve of the machine at will, by manipu-
lating a handwheel, or regulator. A typical range of characteristics is shown in Fig. 2.

Engine-driven Sets.—Engine-driven sets are useful in
cases where no mains supply is available.

These may be driven by either a petrol or Diesel engine.
For works and isolated situations where no electric power is
available, there is naturally no alternative to an engine-driven
set.

352

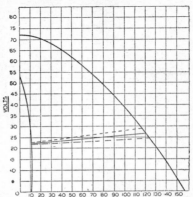

Fig. 2.—Typical Characteristic Curve Range of Welding Generator.

Plant of this description with a petrol engine has the advantage of lower first cost and total weight, but the Diesel-engine driven plant is now becoming popular owing to its extremely low running cost, and to the fact that it can be relied upon to give good service under almost any conditions.

Most engine-driven sets are required as portable units. Therefore, in order to keep the weight, dimensions and running costs down to a minimum they should be limited to one or two operators.

When necessary, two drooping characteristic dynamos can be built into one frame, in order to conserve space, but it would not be a practicable proposition to have more than two in tandem, and it is for that reason that a portable engine-driven set should never be specified for more than two welders.

Capacities of Welding Dynamos.—With regard to capacity, a single-operator 200-A. machine will fulfil most requirements for general repair and fabrication work, but when it is desired to provide for two men, the ideal is a double dynamo, as described above, each half having an output of 200 A., but so arranged that they can be easily and quickly put in parallel to give up to 400 A. to one man when necessary. In this connection it may be mentioned that a great deal of research work is now being undertaken by electrode manufacturers relative to high-speed welding by

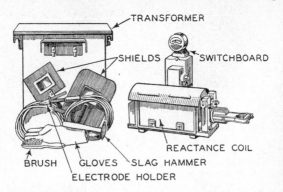

FIG. 3.—Equipment for Alternating Current Welding.

means of special electrodes requiring much larger currents than have been used in the past, and many large engineering concerns have already installed the necessary welding plant to enable them to take advantage of this development and thus speed up production.

Therefore, a double dynamo can be considered most elastic in its uses, as by a touch of a switch it can be instantly converted from a two-operator 200-A. set into a single-operator 400-A. machine for high-speed welding.

A.C. Welding Equipment.—A.C. welding equipment comprises a step-down transformer provided with suitable regulating equipment.

From Fig. 3 it will be observed that the necessary regulation is provided by a reactance coil.

Static transformer sets again have certain advantages and disadvantages.

This type of plant can be obtained at a comparatively low initial cost, and has the advantage of high overall electrical efficiency, and maintenance charges are reduced to a minimum as there are no rotating parts.

Its welding performance is equal to that of a generator giving direct current, and is not recommended for overhead welding, unless special electrodes are used ; bare wires should never be used with a transformer plant.

Electrodes for Metallic Arc Welding.—Electrodes used for arc welding are of three types :—

    (a) Bare wire rods.
    (b) Dipped or lightly covered electrodes.
    (c) Heavy-coated electrodes.

Bare electrodes are usually run at a lower welding voltage. Welding currents range from 150 to 300 amperes according to the size of electrode used. With bare electrodes (Fig. 4) more difficulty is experienced in starting the arc.

Light-covered or dipped electrodes provide better protection against oxidation of the weld. They are considered an improvement on bare electrodes and require a higher welding voltage and lower current than the bare rods.

Heavy-coated electrodes are coated with a material of substantial thickness and solidity, calculated to provide protection to the electrode. Figs. 5 and 6 illustrate this principle.

Flux-covered electrodes have in general a spiral winding of asbestos yarn as the basis of the covering. Asbestos is a valuable flux in itself, as it fuses and combines with iron oxide into a compound silicate which, being very light and mobile, is easily removed after solidification, leaving a clean surface— an important advantage for work which requires more than one run of welding. Asbestos yarn also makes an excellent vehicle and support for the other constituents of the covering, and with a suitable binder makes a tough-surfaced sheath to the metal core. These electrodes, therefore, travel and handle without loss and damage.

Bare or lightly dipped electrodes are operated on the negative pole. Heavily coated electrodes, especially those with asbestos covers, are generally used on the positive pole.

Electrodes for Carbon Arc Welding.—For welding light-gauge metal a carbon electrode is sometimes used. In certain cases no filler rod is required, the heat of the arc being sufficient to melt the material which is being welded. In other cases a

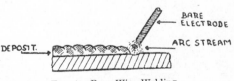

Fig. 4.—Bare Wire Welding.

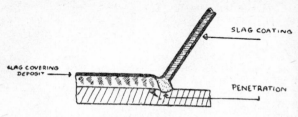

FIG. 5.—Welding with a Coated Electrode.

light filler rod may be fed into the weld as the work progresses. When using the carbon arc welding process it is advisable to use a special electrode holder, which contains a coil through which the main current passes. This has the effect of steadying the arc which may be deflected away from the work if such control is not provided.

Amongst skilled welders the carbon arc process is often used for the repair of cast iron, using a high silicon cast-iron filler rod, where the work can previously be preheated. It is also used for the welding of non-magnetic materials, as aluminium, copper, bronze, brass, "Everdur," and such metals.

Another application being used more and more is the welding of light-gauge mild steel in, say, 14-, 16-, and 18-gauge sheet metal by the carbon arc at low current values, employing a manual electrode holder providing in itself magnetic control. In this form it is also used in the welding of certain stainless steels.

Current Values for Arc Welding.—The following table shows recommended values of currents to be used with different sizes of welding electrode.

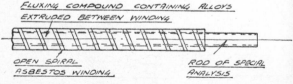

FIG. 6.—A Special Type of Coating for Heavy-coated Electrodes.

Gauge.	Averages Recommended.	Maximum.
4 S.W.G.	200 amps.	270 amps.
6 ,,	170 ,,	200 ,,
8 ,,	140 ,,	170 ,,
10 ,,	115 ,,	130 ,,
12 ,,	70 ,,	90 ,,
14 ,,	45 ,,	65 ,,

Welding Accessories.—In addition to the different types of welding plant described above, the following accessories should form a part of every operator's equipment.

One electrode holder, fitted with a length of flexible cable to connect to plant.

One length of flexible cable, for connecting the job to the plant.

One face screen, complete with coloured glasses.

One observer's face screen, with coloured glasses.

One pair of leather gauntlet gloves.

One chipping hammer, to remove slag from weld.

One wire brush, to clean the weld after chipping.

A face screen, or helmet, should be made from fibre or other non-conducting material and should have no screws or rivets that *go right through* the insulating material from which they are made. This is an important feature, as otherwise there is a risk of the operator receiving an unpleasant, if not dangerous, shock in the face should he accidentally touch such pieces of metal with his electrode holder.

ATOMIC HYDROGEN ARC WELDING

The essentials of the atomic-hydrogen arc-welding process are : (1) electrical energy is supplied to an arc between two tungsten electrodes where it is transformed into heat ; (2) molecular hydrogen is blown through this arc and transformed catalytically into the atomic form which acts as a vehicle for transfer of energy from the arc to the work ; and (3) in the direction away from the arc a sudden decrease of temperature (such as that obtained at the relative cold surface of the weld area) causes the rapid decrease in the concentration of atomic hydrogen and a release of the heat of recombination.

Equipment.—The apparatus required consists of a source of power for maintaining the arc between the two tungsten electrodes, a supply of hydrogen to be passed through this arc, and a holder for the tungsten electrodes.

The source of power could be either d.c. or a.c., but a.c. supply was chosen because it is more commonly available,

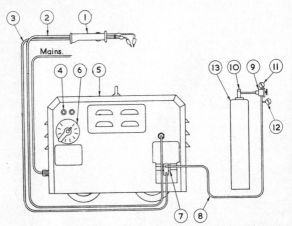

Fig. 7.—Diagram of Atomic Hydrogen Arc Welding Plant.

(1) Torch. (2) Torch cable. (3) Torch gas tube. (4) Push-buttons. (5) Welding set. (6) Tapping switch. (7) Auto hydrogen valve. (8) Gas tube. (9) Auto regulating valve. (10) Hydrogen cylinder valve. (11, 12) Pressure gauges. (13) Hydrogen cylinder.

(A.E.I. Ltd.)

the electrodes are consumed equally (not the case with d.c.), and finally its efficiency is higher. Whilst varying the current can be done with d.c. by the use of resistances, the method is wasteful in energy and far less efficient than the variable reactance used with a.c.

To strike and maintain the arc, an open-circuit voltage of 300-volt is necessary and for hand welding a current range up to 50-amp is required. This power is obtained from a transformer having a number of primary tappings to allow

FIG. 8.—Wiring
Diagram for
50A Atomic
Hydrogen Welder.

C.   Contactor.
MV. Magnet valve.
Opc. Operating coil.
R.   Relay.
TS. Tapping switch.
Rf. Rectifier.

(A.E.I. Ltd.)

for various supply voltages and a tapped reactor to permit adjustment of the current. The tappings on this reactor are selected by a tapping switch.

A complete equipment for atomic hydrogen welding by hand is shown in Fig. 7, and the wiring diagram is shown in Fig. 8. Power is switched on by a push-button; this operation closes a contactor which remains held in when the arc is struck. When the arc is extinguished, by either pressing the stop-button or increasing the gap between the electrodes, the contactor opens, thus taking power off the electrode holder and so rendering the torch dead. It is impossible for the operator to receive a shock, as the power is on only when the start-button is depressed (i.e. one of his hands is occupied) or when the arc is struck (i.e. when the uninsulated part of the holder is too near the arc to be touched). The hydrogen is passed through a 2-stage regulator and a solenoid valve which allows it to flow only when the arc is established.

ARGONARC WELDING PROCESS

The Argonarc welding process is a method of joining non-ferrous metals and stainless and high alloy steels without using flux. An electric arc struck between an electrode and the work-piece produces the heat to fuse the material and the electrode and the weld area are shielded from the atmosphere by means of an inert gas (argon). Standard d.c. or a.c. welding equipment may be used provided the open circuit voltage is around 100 V for a.c. and 70 V for d.c.

For welding aluminium, magnesium and their alloys, stainless and high alloy steels, nickel alloys and copper alloys, up to $\frac{1}{8}$ in. thick, a.c. is suitable. D.c. may be used for all other common metals, and it is essential for the welding of copper and stainless steels and alloys over $\frac{1}{8}$ in. thick.

Method of Welding.—The argon is supplied to the torch through p.v.c. tubing, where it is directed round the tungsten electrode and over the weld area by either a ceramic or water-cooled copper shield.

The torch is held (or clamped) so that the electrode is at approximately 80° to the weld and travels in a leftward direction. Filler wire may be added to reinforce the weld, the angle being approximately 20° to the seam. It is important that the end of the filler wire should be pressed on to the workpiece and be fed into the front edge of the weld pool.

When comparatively long straight seams are to be welded, e.g. jointing sheets, strip, or fabricating cylindrical vessels, argonarc machine welding may be used. Much of this type of work is done without using filler wire, i.e. the butted edges are simply fused together. Where maximum strength or a flush surface is required or when material over $\frac{1}{8}$ in. thick is being welded, filler wire may be added.

Argonarc Spot Welding.—This is a supplementary process to resistance spot welding, and is used to make spot welds in positions inaccessible to resistance spot welders.

In principle, a local fusion takes place between the sheets to be joined. The torch, which is hand-controlled, contains a tungsten electrode recessed within a water-cooled shield. Argon gas is used to shield the electrode and weld area.

A trigger switch in the torch handle initiates the weld sequence which is controlled by a timing control cabinet. The two sheets are pressed together, using the nozzle of the torch, and then the operator should squeeze and release the trigger. An arc is struck for the pre-set time and the sheets fuse together under the electrode. The top sheet must not exceed 16 s.w.g., but material up to this gauge may be joined to plate or thicker sections.

The process can be used on stainless steels, bright mild and alloy steels and some nickel and copper alloys.

Argonaut Welding.—This is a manual (Argonarc) inert gas shielded metallic arc process, but with a consumable electrode and automatic regulation.

A thin filler wire is automatically fed through the torch or welding gun at comparatively high speed. A d.c. arc struck between the end of the wire and the work-piece produces the heat which melts the wire and forms the weld pool. The current density in the wire has to be very high in order to project the filler metal across the arc gap, e.g. at least 50,000 A. per square inch in the case of aluminium. The whole weld area is protected by argon.

The process is employed chiefly for light alloy structural fabrication and welding of heavy sections of the metals referred to under Argonarc welding.

RESISTANCE WELDING

Resistance welding differs entirely from arc welding, in the fact that the welding effect is obtained by passing a very heavy current through the two components which are to be welded together. The high resistance at the point of contact causes great heat to be generated, this being sufficient to cause fusion of the contact surfaces. Figs. 9–14 show the main types of resistance welding.

Mechanical Timing.—The accepted method of doing this is to mount a robust switch on the body or rocking arm of the welder and to operate this by a trip or trigger mechanism. The trip closes a switch at some point at the start of the stroke, after an initial pressure has been applied to the weld, and opens at a point near the end of the stroke while the pressure is held on the work. This is suitable for small machines where really high-quality work is not required and it has largely been replaced by the electromagnetic contactor.

Electromagnetic Contactors.—An electromagnetic contactor is used to switch the supply to the primary of the welding transformer. The electromagnetic contactor is closed

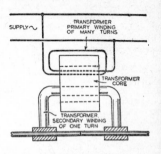

Fig. 9.—Butt Welding Two Steel Rods.

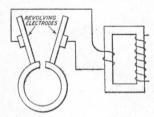

Fig. 10.—Principle of Butt Seam Welding.

When the pieces of work meet edge to edge and are progressively butt welded, the weld is termed a butt seam weld. The electrodes are usually in the form of wheels, as shown, revolving along the length of the work.

(*Patented process by Tube Products Ltd.*)

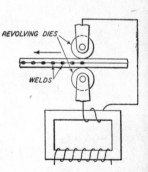

Fig. 11.—Principle of Lap Seam Welding.

The revolving electrodes or dies traverse the length of the lapped plate and produce a series of intermittent or overlapping spot welds on the work.

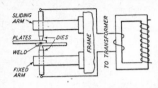

Fig. 12.—Principle of Spot Welding.

The machine consists fundamentally of a transformer, a press and electrodes or dies bearing on the work. The lower electrode is usually fixed, the upper being arranged to move down on to the work.

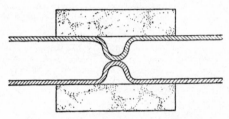

Fig. 13.—Principle of Projection Welding.

The two electrodes clamp the work, as in the case of the spot welder; but when current passes, great heat is generated at the points of the depressions in the metal sheets, which become plastic before being finally urged flatly together by the electrodes. It is quite usual for only one of the two work-pieces to be provided with depressions.

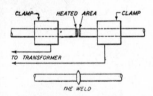

Fig. 14.—Principle of Flash Welding.

The parts to be joined are clamped strongly and are brought close enough together to create an arcing effect. So much heat is developed as to melt the ends of the pieces to be joined. The current is then switched off and the parts are quickly pushed together. The molten metal is forced to the outside, bringing together the metal behind it which is in a plastic condition.

by energizing its coil via a pneumatic or other form of timer. If a thyratron timer is used precise control of welding times from 0·1 second upwards is possible. When a large electromagnetic contactor is used there may be several cycles operating lag in the contactor itself. One particular model of the thyratron timer takes care of this by starting the timed period when the contactor is closed.

Thyratron and Ignitron Control of Resistance Welding.—One of the most important developments in resistance welding has been the application of the thyratron and ignitron tubes for the control of the duration and strength of the current, during the welding operation. The construction and operating characteristics on these two devices are explained in the chapter on electronics which begins on page 24.

Ignitron Contactor.—Contact wear is severe on an electromagnetic contactor used to switch heavy inductive loads, such as a welding transformer, and the inertia of the contactor prevents very short welding times being used. These difficulties are overcome by using the ignitron contactor. This consists of two ignitrons connected in reverse parallel, i.e. the anode of one connected to the cathode of the other. The ignitron consists of an anode, and a mercury pool cathode, but instead of a grid, it has an ignitor. The electrodes are housed in an evacuated steel envelope which is provided with a water jacket for cooling purposes. Some smaller ignitrons, made in glass, are usually fan cooled. The ignitor, which is conical in shape, and is made of semi-conducting material, is permanently immersed, tip downwards, in the mercury pool cathode. When a current impulse is passed through the ignitor into the pool cathode, a " hot spot " is produced at the surface of the pool cathode. This provides a source of electrons, which, if the anode is at a positive potential with respect to the cathode, will be attracted to the anode.

The current will then flow through the ignitron from anode to cathode. When connected in reverse parallel each ignitron is provided with its own ignitor-control circuit. No timing device is provided as an integral part of the equipment, but any suitable timer, preferably electronic, may be used to time the welding period. When a circuit is made between the control terminals, the ignitrons will pass current to the welding machine, and the current flow will cease when the timing device opens a circuit between the control terminals.

Synchronous electronic controls are used to exploit the full capabilities of the ignitron contactor and to enable metals

just described, and require temporary current and potential electrodes. They are, moreover, extremely simple to use, contain their own testing supply and give directly the value of an earth resistance in ohms without any calculations.

The Series 1 tester is a combined ohmmeter and generator of a special type, so designed that alternating current is passed through the soil while direct current is passed through the measuring instrument. The ohmmeter embodies two coils, mounted at a fixed angle to one another on a common axle, moving in the field of a permanent magnet. A current proportional to the total current flowing in the testing circuit passes through the current coil, while the potential coil carries a current proportional to the potential drop across the resistance under test. The coils are so wound that the resulting forces oppose one another.

The final position of the moving coils, and hence that of the pointer, depends on the ratio of the potential drop to the total current, and the instrument is therefore a true ohmmeter giving readings in ohms, which are independent of the applied voltage.

The connections are shown in Fig. 3. Direct current from the generator passes through the current coil of the ohmmeter to a rotating current reverser driven from the generator handle. Alternating current is thus delivered to the current terminals (the common terminal C_1 and C_2 in the diagram) of the instrument, which are connected to the contact under test and to the " current " temporary earth connection. The potential coil of the ohmmeter obtains its supply from the potential terminals (the common terminal P_1 and the terminal P_2 in the diagram), the latter being connected to the " potential " temporary earth connection. Since this supply is taken from the " soil " section of the current circuit and is therefore alternating, it must be made unidirectional before passing through the potential coil. A commutator mounted on the same shaft as the main current reverser, and synchronized with it, is therefore interposed as a rectifier between the potential terminals and the potential coil.

In this manner the current and potential coils of the ohmmeter are both supplied with direct current, and the " soil " section of the testing circuit is supplied with alternating current.

The second earth tester is known as the Null-balance unit. Fig. 4 shows the principle of operation, the range connections having been omitted for simplicity. From this diagram it

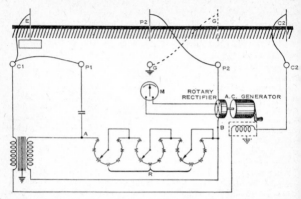

FIG. 4.—Simplified Circuit of the Null Balance Megger Earth Tester.

will be seen that a.c. from the hand generator passes through
the primary of the current transformer to the electrode
under test, E, returning through the soil to terminal $C2$.

The current from the secondary of the transformer produces
a potential difference between A and B, which is adjusted
by the resistance R until it is equal and opposite to the a.c.
potential between $P1$ and $P2$. Balance is shown by a null
reading of the d.c. micro-ammeter M, the current in the
latter being rectified by the rotary rectifier on the generator
shaft.

The adjustable resistance R consists of three decade resistances the total value in the circuit being indicated by a
row of figures. The actual resistance measured is this value
multiplied by the range factor in use. Thus, if balance is
obtained with the digits reading 3, 7, and 6, and the range
switch is at 0·01, then the electrode resistance measured is
3·76 ohms.

An advantage of the null-balance method is that at the
point of balance no current flows through the potential
electrode $P2$ so that its resistance does not affect the reading.

The guard circuit G is a refinement to eliminate effects due
to possible insulation or capacitance leaks in the instrument.

With both the Series I tester and this instrument, the
effect of stray alternating currents in the soil will cause the
pointer to waver at certain handle speeds. In such cases, it

is only necessary to increase or decrease the speed of the generator handle to obtain a steady reading.

Method of Use.—When testing with an earth tester the spacing of the temporary electrodes is of the utmost importance, as the two resistance areas must not overlap.

As a rough guide the following figures may be of assistance. When testing an earth electrode consisting of a single driven pipe or a single earth plate, the current electrode should be about 100 feet from the electrode under test, the potential electrode being about 50 feet away. If the earth electrode is large or consists of several pipes or plates in parallel, these distances should be increased to, say, 150 and 75 feet respectively. Greater distances than these must be used for a complex earth consisting of, say, a large number of pipes or plates and other metallic structures all bonded together.

Drive the temporary current electrode into the ground at a distance from the earth electrode under test which is considered sufficient. Take three readings with the potential electrode driven in at three points in turn, one mid-way between the earth electrode under test and the current electrode, a second 10 feet nearer the earth electrode under test, and a third 10 feet nearer the current electrode. If the three readings so obtained agree with one another within the accuracy required for the measurement, the mean of these three values may be taken as the resistance of the earth connection. If, however, the agreement is not sufficiently close, the current electrode should be moved and driven into the earth at a greater distance from the electrode under test. The three readings should then be taken again. The whole process should be repeated until the three readings obtained with the one setting of the current electrode agree within the limits of accuracy required for the measurement.

The potential electrode must be placed in a direct line between the current electrode and the electrode under test.

For temporary electrodes it is recommended that half an inch diameter solid mild steel spikes, 18 inches in length, should be used. If these are pointed at one end they must be driven into the soil to a depth of 12 inches with a $2\frac{1}{2}$ lb. hammer.

EARTH LOOP TESTING

As already pointed out, one of the functions of earthing is to allow sufficient current to pass in the event of an earth fault so that the protective gear can operate. To allow this current to flow, the resistance of the earth-fault loop must be sufficiently low to suit the requirements of any particular installation.

The earth-fault (or line-earth) loop comprises the line conductor from the point of fault back to the supply transformer, the path through the transformer winding, the earthed neutral point of the transformer, the path from that point to the consumer's earthing lead, the earthing lead and the earth-continuity conductor back to the point of fault.

Instruments are now available for measuring the complete earth-fault loop and provided the results so obtained are

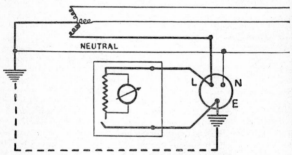

NEUTRAL

L

N

E

Fig. 5.—Method of carrying out a Line-Earth Loop Test.

satisfactory no further tests are necessary. Where, however, the value of the loop is too high the cause has to be investigated and tests have to be made of the resistance to earth of the electrodes themselves and of the earthing leads and continuity conductors.

Line-earth Loop Test.—The object of this test is to measure the actual earth-fault loop through which the fault current would pass. One of the instruments designed for making this test is the Megger Line-Earth Loop tester. This instrument which operates on full mains voltage, passes a short duration current of about 20 A from the line conductor through the consumer's earth continuity conductor and the

must not be less than 0·5 megohm to earth and between poles or phases.

Testing Motors and Generators.—It is important to make regular tests of the insulation resistance of all machinery so as to detect incipient faults. It is best to make the test of a machine as soon after it has been shut down as possible, when the insulation resistance is likely to be lowest.

How to make Tests on Motors and Generators.—
(a) *D.C. Motors and Generators.*—Disconnect the supply of electricity from the motor circuit by opening the main switch and withdrawing the main fuses.

Join together both terminals on the motor side of the double pole main switch (Fig. 2) and connect these to one terminal of the "Megger" Insulation Tester.

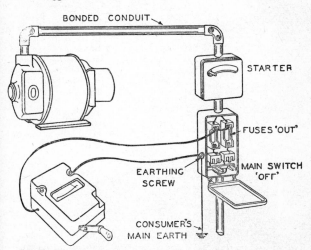

FIG. 2.—Test to Frame or Earth on Motor and Switchgear.

Connect the other terminal of the "Megger" Tester to earth, using the frame of the motor and panel. Turn the generator handle at 160 r.p.m., and take a reading.

If the insulation resistance between the terminals and the frames is found to be unsatisfactory, it must be ascertained

381

whether the fault is on the starter, the motor, or the cables connecting the starter to the motor.

To do this, disconnect the cables at the motor, and repeat the test. If this disconnection shows that the fault has been cleared, then it is evident that the fault does not lie in the starter but in the motor.

Repeat the test on the motor only.

1. With the armature and field windings all connected together (Fig. 3).
2. With the brushes lifted from contact with the commutator (Fig. 4).
3. On the armature only, between the commutator and frame, the brushes being lifted (Fig. 5).

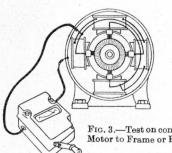

FIG. 3.—Test on complete Motor to Frame or Earth.

BRUSHES LIFTED OFF COMMUTATOR.

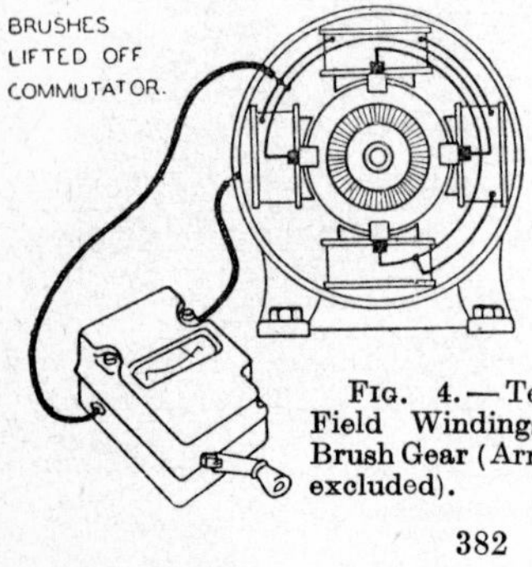

FIG. 4.—Test on Field Windings and Brush Gear (Armature excluded).

From these tests it can be deduced whether the fault is in the field coils and brush gear, in the armature or in both.

If the fault is not in the armature, separate out sections of the windings and components and test individually until the defect is located.

Similarly, if the defect was originally traced to the starter, separate out the various coils such as resistance coils, no-volt release coil and overload coil and test these separately.

In the above description a simple rheostat starter has been taken to illustrate the principles of fault location. The exact procedure will vary with the type of the starter. Thus with a contactor operated starter which, in the " off " position, disconnects *all* the lines to the motor, it is necessary to make tests to earth on both the incoming and

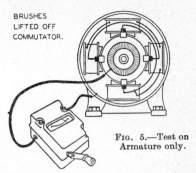

BRUSHES
LIFTED OFF
COMMUTATOR.

Fig. 5.—Test on Armature only.

outgoing terminals of the starter.

It is sometimes found that the insulation resistance is low all round without a definite fault on any section. This can usually be remedied by careful cleaning of the machine, for, when electrical machinery has been in service some time, it is liable to become coated in places with metallic or other conducting dust, often mixed with oil, from commutators or slip rings. Such deposits form leakage paths.

(*b*) *A.C. Motors and Generators.*—These should be tested in a similar manner to d.c. machines, isolating the various circuits until the fault is located. With polyphase machines the starters should be fastened in the " on " position before making a test (the main switch being off).

Insulation Values.—The British Standard Specification No. 170 for fractional horse-power generators and motors lays down that the insulation resistance shall be not less than 1 megohm when testing with 500 volts d.c. For large industrial generators and motors no value is laid down for the insulation resistance as this will vary with the conditions in which the test is carried out. However, as a rough guide, the insulation resistance for large machines, when tested at 500 volts d.c., should not be less in megohms than :

$$\frac{\text{rated voltage}}{1{,}000 + \text{rated output in kVA or BHP}}.$$

When a test is made on a new machine, this figure must be obtained at the end of a run at full load, when the machine is hot and the insulation resistance is likely to be at the lowest value.

BATTERY ELECTRIC VEHICLES

ONE of the chief advantages of battery electric vehicles is the absence of noise and fumes and they therefore are finding an increasing use in factories, hospitals and, to a lesser extent, city centres. There are a considerable number of different types of battery-electric vehicles but only the most important are mentioned here.

Light Delivery Vehicles.—Battery electric vehicles are widely recognized as suitable for tradesmen's delivery rounds, and several makers have specialized in this type. Vehicles are made suitable for pay loads ranging from 3 cwt. to 30 cwt. According to the type of vehicle, the battery capacity varies between 210 and 330 Ah.

The type of controller fitted depends upon the kind of duty the vehicle is intended for. There are at least three different types of control available, namely resistance ; parallel-series system of battery connection ; and electronic or transistorized method. In the first, used by the Morrison Electricar, the resistance is inserted or taken out of the motor circuit by electromagnetic contactors fitted with blow-out coils. A simple plunger type foot-operated master switch (i.e. accelerator) operates the contactors in sequence, the acceleration being controlled automatically by pneumatic time-delay switches activated by the contactors. A separate forward/reverse switch and key-type removable isolating switch are provided.

The parallel-series system enables either half or full voltage to be applied to the motor simply by connecting the two " halves " of the battery either in parallel or series. It will be seen that with this arrangement there is still need for some resistance to vary the voltage between the two extremes available.

A recent development is the transistorized controller which passes current to the motor in rapid oscillations, the frequency of these pulses being governed by the position of the accelerator. Thus at full speed the current flow is continuous.

Whilst such vehicles find their greatest use for tradesmen, they are also employed for ambulances, mini-buses, factory run-abouts and occasionally refuse-collectors. Increasing attention is being paid to their use in the maintenance of street-lighting units where their quiet operation is suitable for late-night work.

Electric Crane Trucks.—These have been designed to carry $1\frac{1}{2}$ tons and to lift $\frac{1}{2}$ ton. Two independent totally-enclosed 1-h.p. motors for traction are bolted to the front swivel stub axle, a double helical pinion on each motor engaging with an internal helical ring secured to the road wheel. A combination drum-type controller is fitted having simple forward, neutral and reverse positions, while a pedal-operated rheostatic starter is so arranged that when the pedal is depressed the brake is released and the circuit completed, and vice versa.

The hoist motion is powered by a 2-h.p. motor running at 1,800 r.p.m., the derricking being also effected by means of the hoisting rope. The bob weight is brought into contact with the jib head and hoisting converted into a derricking motion. Slewing is effected by hand, the jib being capable of describing an angle of 180 deg.

Fixed Platform Trucks.—Fixed platform trucks are available capable of carrying loads from 5 cwt to 3 tons and are fitted with totally-enclosed series-wound motors. Controllers for trucks up to 20 cwt are of the hand-operated drum type, giving three speeds forward and reverse, with series-parallel resistance field control. In the case of trucks taking from $1\frac{1}{2}$ to 3 tons, hand-operated contactor type controllers are fitted, the contactors being operated by a cam and trigger arrangement. The controller provides for three speeds forward and three reverse. The controller, together with the resistance, ampere-hour meter and charging socket, are all housed in the control column, and the arrangement is such that the controller handle must be in the neutral position after the foot-brake has been applied before the truck can be restarted. The 5-cwt trucks are provided with 15 cells, giving an ampere-hour capacity at the 5-hour rate of 81, while the 3-ton trucks have 20 cells, giving a capacity of 243 ampere-hours.

Fixed platform trucks are available for pedestrian control or for carrying a driver either seated or standing. The latest development in this line however is the driverless truck. This is an electronically-controlled vehicle which follows the path of an electrical conductor laid in or on the floor. Signal current in the conductor of approximately $\frac{1}{2}$ A at a specified frequency is sensed by a device in the truck which keeps it on the desired path. There is no physical contact between the truck and the guide wire. The running, braking and starting of the truck is controlled from a convenient point. It stops automatically on lightly striking any obstruction in the path.

Tractors or Tugs.—Tractors or tugs do not themselves carry a load, unless working as an articulated unit. Their purpose is to pull trailers or trolleys which can be single units or in numbers forming a train of towed trailers, arranged for easy and quick coupling one to the other.

Electric tractors are available in a wide variety and are capable of pulling many tons. Special designs are obtainable for use in narrow aisles, and for outdoor use, the manufacturers can supply units with suitable wheels and of higher speeds. Besides the manufacturing industry they have been employed in hospitals, warehouses, railways and dockside service.

Lansing Bagnall have a range of four tractors suitable for a maximum drawbar pull of 500 lb for the smallest, up to 2 500 lb for the largest. An electro-pneumatic drive system for both front and rear wheels is employed and the unladen travel speed is 7·25 m.p.h. for the small tractor and 13 m.p.h. for the largest. Capacities of the batteries range from 145 Ah up to 334 Ah but still larger batteries can be fitted if required.

Fork-lift Trucks.—This particular truck has been designed for lifting and handling loaded pallets or unit loads of similar character and conveying them to machines, or to stores, loading on to road vehicles or railway wagons. Counter-balanced fork-lift trucks are available with capacities of up to 6 000 lb.

The lifting mechanism provides for the forks to be moved up or down a telescopic type mast or similar design ; all combine a degree of forward or backward tilting movement to facilitate picking up, unloading and carrying with safety. The distance between the forks is adjustable to suit different loads and forks of different lengths and types are available.

Either 3- or 4-wheeled trucks are made, the former usually having a smaller handling capacity but possessing a very much smaller turning radius. For outside work trucks are available with unladen speeds of up to 14 m.p.h. dropping to 11 m.p.h. with a 4 000 lb load.

Pedestrian controlled or driver-platform types can be provided and special narrow units are made for use in narrow aisles. Lifting heights exceed 10 ft. in many cases.

Battery capacities range from 167 Ah at 24 V for the pedestrian-controlled units up to 754 Ah at 24 V.

The pallet and stillage trucks are a slight variation to the fork-lift truck. Instead of a platform they have two flat arms projecting forward in the manner of forks but supported at their forward ends by very small-diameter wheels, and this allows them to run under a pallet and its load. Battery power enables the load to be lifted off the ground for transportation. These trucks are available for pedestrian or driver control.

There are also a number of other types of materials-handling truck but space does not permit a description of them. Examples are elevating platform trucks and automatic mobile tipplers.

Battery-driven Electric Locomotives.—The characteristics of battery-electric vehicles makes them ideally suitable for use as underground locomotives where their fumeless features are advantageous. At the time of writing the National Coal Board has about 400 of them in service of varying sizes up to 90 h.p. Battery-driven electric locomotives are also suitable for shunting work above as well as below ground, particularly for factories already using fixed-platform trucks, because the battery-charging facilities will be available.

Battery Charging.—Several types of battery chargers have been designed to meet the requirements of those running either a single electric vehicle or a fleet of vehicles. The most popular types employ the dry-plate rectifier and transformer. A typical unit consists of a double-wound air-cooled transformer normally wound for 200–250 volts and the selenium rectifying unit. The primary of the transformer is provided with a tapping to compensate for the slight ageing of the rectifier, which is inherent after about 10,000 hours' duty. The rectifier is bridge-connected and a four-position switch used in conjunction with tappings in the secondary of the transformer allows for adjustment of the normal or equalizing charge, according to the characteristics of the battery.

The standard range is for use with lead-acid batteries of 24–30 cells, the charging rates varying between 15 and 30 amperes.

INDEX